AQA GCSE Design and Technology

Resistant Materials

Orders: please contact Bookpoint Ltd, 130 Milton Park, Abingdon, Oxon OX14 4SB. Telephone: +44 (0)1235 827720. Fax: +44 (0)1235 400454. Lines are open from 9.00–5.00, Monday to Saturday, with a 24-hour message-answering service. You can also order through our website www.hoddereducation.co.uk

If you have any comments to make about this, or any of our other titles, please send them to educationenquiries@hodder.co.uk

British Library Cataloguing in Publication Data

A catalogue record for this title is available from the British Library

ISBN: 978 1 444 12366 1

First Edition Published 2011
This Edition Published 2011
Impression number   10 9 8 7 6 5 4 3 2 1
Year   2016, 2015, 2014, 2013, 2012, 2011

Hachette UK's policy is to use papers that are natural, renewable and recyclable products and made from wood grown in sustainable forests. The logging and manufacturing processes are expected to conform to the environmental regulations of the country of origin.

Cover photo from © allOver photography/Alamy

Typeset by DC Graphic Design Limited, Swanley Village, Kent

Printed in Italy for Hodder Education, an Hachette UK Company, 338 Euston Road, London NW1 3BH

AQA GCSE Design and Technology

GET BETTER RESULTS FOR AQA

Resistant Materials

series editor: **Bryan Williams**

Paul Anderson
Stuart Douglas
Ryan Lemon
Marianne Starkie
Steve Smith

HODDER
EDUCATION
AN HACHETTE UK COMPANY

Contents

Acknowledgements

The authors would like to thank Ripley St. Thomas CE High School, Lancaster and St. Edmund Arrowsmith Catholic High School, Wigan for providing examples of student Controlled Assessment work.

The authors and publishers would like to thank the following for the use of photographs in this book.

Figure 1.2 RTimages – Fotolia; Figure 1.3 Eugene Skidanov – Fotolia; Figure 1.4 Elena Butinova – Fotolia; Figure 1.5 Forest Stewardship Council UK; Figure 1.12 zmkstudio – Fotolia; Figure 1.19 Ian Holland – Fotolia; Figure 1.21 EYE OF SCIENCE/ SCIENCE PHOTO LIBRARY; Figure 1.22 RTimages/iStockphoto.com; Figure 1.26 ril – Fotolia; Figure 1.31 Ilja Maölk – Fotolia; Figure 2.5 Imagesource/Photolibrary Group; Figure 2.6 Ni Chun – Fotolia; Figure 2.7 © Richard Heyes/Alamy; Figure 2.8 Popova Olga – Fotolia; Figure 2.9 Andres Rodriguez – Fotolia; Figure 2.10 tbel – Fotolia; Figure 2.13 BMW AG; Figure 2.14 Justin Sullivan/Getty Images; Figure 3.1 Pli Design Ltd; Figure 3.2 © Peter Alvey/Alamy; Figure 3.3 Mark Boulton/Photolibrary Group; Figure 3.5 © Gary Unwin – Fotolia.com; Figure 3.6 manfredxy – Fotolia; Figure 3.7 drimi – Fotolia; Figure 3.8 © dbimages/Alamy; Figure 3.9 Stephen Wilson/PA Archive/Press Association Images; Figure 3.10 Pierre brillot – Fotolia; Figure 3.12 EU Ecolabel; Figure 6.1 Dream-Emotion – Fotolia; Figure 6.2 photlook – Fotolia; Figure 6.3 Rainer Plendl – Fotolia; Figure 6.4 AVAVA – Fotolia; Figure 6.5 Delphimages – Fotolia; Figure 7.1 iQoncept – Fotolia; Figure 7.2 Yuri Arcurs – Fotolia; Figure 7.3 Paul Maguire – Fotolia; Figure 7.4 Sunny.baby – Fotolia; Figure 7.5 Diamond Sky Images/Iconica/Getty Images; Figure 7.6 © Pali Rao/iStockphoto.com; Figure 7.7 © Jacob Wackerhausen; Figure 8.6 © Powered by Light RF/Alamy; Figure 8.9 Fairtrade Foundation; Figure 11.3 Boxford Ltd; Figure 13.4 Terry Bream; Figure 13.7 Terry Bream; Figure 13.8 Terry Bream; Figure 13.11 Terry Bream; Figure 13.12 Terry Bream; battery in Table 13.1 on page 161 Terry Morris – Fotolia; microphone in Table 13.1 on page162 LoopAll – Fotolia; lamp in Table 13.1 on page162 gemenacom – Fotolia; other photos in Table 13.1 Terry Bream; Figure 14.1 Diamond Sky Images/Iconica/Getty Images; Figure 14.7 TechSoft UK Ltd.; Figure 14.8 TechSoft UK Ltd.; Figure 14.9 © Onur Döngel/iStockphoto.com; Figure 14.10 TechSoft UK Ltd.; Figure 14.11 Roland; Figure 14.12 TechSoft UK Ltd.; Figure 14.14 Roland; Figure 14.15 TechSoft UK Ltd.; Figure 15.1 NASA; Figure 15.2 Photodisc/Getty Images; Figure 15.3 auris – Fotolia; Figure 15.4 © Gene Chutka; Figure 15.5 David Brown Gear Systems Limited; Figure 15.8 © josemoraes/iStockphoto.com; Figure 15.11© YangYin/iStockphoto.com

All other photographs in this volume are supplied by the authors.

Illustrations by Barking Dog Art.

Every effort has been made to trace and acknowledge the ownership of copyright. The publishers will be happy to make arrangements with any copyright owners that it has not been possible to contact.

chapter 1
Materials and components

Introduction

Different materials have different properties. Understanding these properties and how they can be changed helps us to choose the best material for an application.

This chapter deals with a range of resistant materials, including wood, metals, plastics and composites. It outlines how these materials are processed, their typical properties and how they are used.

1.1 **Material properties**

Design needs

When designing a product, a good starting point is to know what the product should be able to do – its performance needs. These will normally be identified by the designer. For example:

○ a table must support the weight that will be put on top of it

○ a fork should not bend when it is pushed into food
○ the wall of a swimming pool must resist damage caused by water.

A single product may have several different performance needs. For example, the table may also have to look good and be low cost.

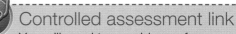

Controlled assessment link
   You will need to consider performance needs as part of your Controlled Assessment. The specifications in Figures 2.19 and 2.20 consider performance needs. The student exemplars in Figures 5.6, 5.7 and 5.11 show how the materials you choose will determine your manufacturing technique.

Material properties

Different materials act in different ways. The way a material acts is referred to as its properties.

These properties will affect how well the product does what it is needed to do, how long the product lasts, its weight and cost.

We need to be sure that the materials we select to make a product are suitable for that product. This means that we must match the properties of the material to the performance needs of the product.

If we understand what the different types of property are, it is easier to understand the differences between various types of material. It will also help us to choose the best materials for a product.

Material properties can be classified as two types: mechanical or physical.

○ Mechanical properties are about how the material reacts when a force is applied to it.
○ Physical properties are characteristics of the material. They are not affected by applying a force to the material.

Mechanical properties
Strength

The strength of a material is its ability to resist breaking or permanently bending when a force is applied to it. There are five different ways in which force can be applied to the material. This means that there are five different types of strength (see Figure 1.1).

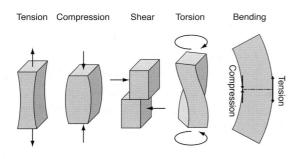

Tension Compression Shear Torsion Bending

△ **Figure 1.1** Types of strength

Hardness

Hardness is the ability of a material to resist cutting, scratches and indentations to its surface.

Toughness

Toughness is the extent to which a material can withstand knocks and blows without breaking. It is the opposite of being brittle.

Elasticity

Elasticity shows how much a material can be stretched or deformed and still return to its original shape.

Ductility

Every material has an elastic limit. When the material is stretched further than its limit, its shape will be changed permanently. Ductility is a measurement of how much the material can be stretched without breaking.

Flexibility

This is how easy the material is to bend without permanently changing shape. If a material is not flexible, it is said to be rigid or stiff.

Malleability

Malleability is the ability for the shape of the material to be permanently changed without breaking. It shows how easy it is to hammer, roll or press a material into a different shape.

Physical properties
Corrosion resistance

The corrosion resistance of a material is its ability to resist being damaged by its environment.

Thermal and electrical conductivity

Thermal and electrical conductivity indicates how easily heat and electricity pass through a material.

Density

The density of the material is how much a certain volume of it weighs. For two objects of the same size, a low-density material will be lightweight and a high-density material will be heavy.

Strength-to-weight ratio

Strength-to-weight ratio is a measure of the strength of the material compared to its weight. For products such as aeroplane wings, the amount of material used will be based on the strength needed by the product. A product made from a material with a high strength-to-weight ratio will weigh less than a product made from material with a low strength-to-weight ratio.

Aesthetic qualities

Aesthetic means how well an object appeals to the five senses. There are a number of aesthetic qualities:

○ what the product looks like – its colour and shape, whether it is shiny or dull

○ whether the surface is rough or smooth to touch – for example, the handle of a tennis racket may be rough to make it easier to grip

○ what the material tastes and smells like – this is important if you are making a bowl to hold food or a toy that a small child might put into its mouth

○ what sound is made by the product – this could be how loud the siren of an alarm is or the musical note made when a bell is struck.

Which aesthetic qualities are important for a product will depend upon what the product is designed to do.

Sustainability

Sustainability indicates how environmentally friendly a material is. This might include:

○ whether the material can be replaced by natural means

○ whether it can be recycled

○ whether it is biodegradable.

Case study

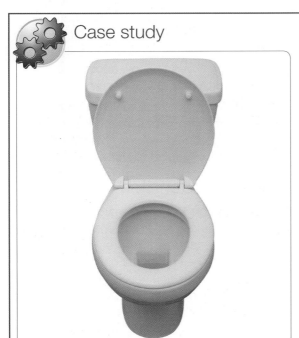

Almost every product is made from materials that were chosen because of their properties. This is true for even the most common objects that we use every day, although we may never have thought about the properties that these products need. For example, the material used for a toilet has to have good compressive strength so that people can sit on it without it breaking. It also needs to have good corrosion resistance and a smooth surface so that it is easy to clean.

△ **Figure 1.2** Toilet: good compressive strength

Cost

Cost is one of the most important properties considered during the design of a product. It can include both the cost of the raw material and the cost of the work needed to change the shape of the material into the required product. Designers sometimes have to make a compromise between other properties and cost. For example, they may have to change a design so that a less strong material is used because it is cheaper.

Controlled assessment link

You will need to consider material properties when designing in your Controlled Assessment work. The page shown in Chapter 4 (Figure 4.7) describes why certain materials have been chosen because of their material properties.

Exam practice questions

1. Identify the material properties that might be important for each of the following products. For each product, put the properties in order of priority – the most important property should be at the top, with the least important at the bottom:

   (a) the frame for an off-road mountain bike

   (b) a tyre for a racing bike

   (c) the body of an electric kettle

   (d) a chair for use in a classroom

   (e) a table for use in a school canteen

   (f) a helmet for a cyclist

   (g) a car bumper

   (h) a satellite dish.

   (i) the body panels on the space shuttle.

2. Using the internet, for each type of property find a test that is used to measure it. You should describe how each test is carried out.

Exam tips

When you are explaining why you have decided to choose a certain material for a product, you should use the names of properties.

1.2 Classifying materials

Materials can be classified into different types. The most common way of grouping them gives five main categories, based on what they were made from:

○ wood

○ metal

○ polymers, also known as plastics

○ ceramics

○ composites.

Composites are a special category, where the material is made from a combination of the other material types.

Ceramic materials include glass and the bricks used to line furnaces. Typically, they have good compressive strength, are very hard but are brittle. They are good thermal and electrical insulators, with excellent corrosion resistance. You are not required to know about ceramic materials within your GCSE course.

Some people think that all materials within each of these categories have similar properties. This is wrong. While there may be some typical properties, there can be big differences between the properties of individual materials within a category.

It is also possible to classify materials in other ways. For example, smart materials are classified as a group of materials based on how their properties can be changed. For the purpose of your GCSE course, you need to know about smart materials but will normally use the above classifications.

1.3 Wood

Wood is probably the oldest material to be used by man. It is still used to make a wide range of products, from the roof beams in houses to decorative dining tables.

Types of wood

There are two 'families' of wood: hardwood and softwood.

Hardwoods come from deciduous trees (see Figure 1.3). These are broad-leaved trees that lose their leaves each autumn. Common hardwoods, shown in Table 1.1, include oak, ash and beech.

Softwoods come from coniferous trees (see Figure 1.4). These are cone-bearing trees that remain green all year round. In general, coniferous trees normally grow faster than deciduous trees. Typical softwoods, shown in Table 1.2, include pine, cedar and redwood.

△ **Figure 1.3** Deciduous tree

△ **Figure 1.4** Coniferous tree

These names do not mean that hardwoods are hard or that softwoods are soft. For example, balsa is a hardwood. However, it is soft enough that if you squeeze it in your hand you can make an impression in it. In comparison, yew is a softwood, but it is hard and flexible.

Name	Source	Properties/working characteristics	Uses
Beech	UK, Europe	Very tough, hard, straight and close-grained; it withstands wear and shocks; polishes well; liable to warp	Chairs, flooring, tools, turnery, toys, steam-bent furniture
Ash	UK, Europe	Wide-grained, tough, very flexible, finishes well	Tool handles, sports equipment including cricket stumps and hockey sticks, ladders
Elm	UK, Europe	Tough, flexible, durable, water-resistant, liable to warp; it can be difficult to work due to its cross-grain	Garden furniture (treated), turnery, interior furniture
Oak	Europe	Heavy, hard, tough, open-grain, finishes well; good outdoors; due to it containing tannic acid it will corrode steel screws, leaving a blue stain	Boat building, floors, gateposts, high-class furniture and fittings
Mahogany	Africa, South America	Easy to work, wide boards available, polishes quite well, but has interlocking grain which makes it difficult to work	Indoor furniture, shop fittings, veneers used to face manufactured boards
Teak	Burma, India	Hard, durable, natural oils resist moisture, fire, acids, alkalis; straight grain, works well; very expensive	Laboratory benches, high-class furniture, veneers, garden furniture, traditional boat decks

△ **Table 1.1** Common hardwoods

Name	Source	Properties/working characteristics	Uses
Redwood (Scots pine)	Northern Europe, Russia	Straight grain, knotty, easy to work, finishes well, durable; widely available and relatively cheap	Most commonly used for construction work; suitable for all inside work but needs protection when used outdoors
Western red cedar	USA, Canada	Lightweight, knot-free, straight grain, contains natural oils that protect from weather, insects, dry rot; fine silky surface	Outdoor joinery, e.g. cladding of buildings, wall panelling
Parana pine	South America	Hard, straight grain, almost knot-free, available in wide boards	Good-quality inside joinery such as staircases and built-in furniture

△ **Table 1.2** Common softwoods

Contd

Name	Source	Properties/working characteristics	Uses
Whitewood (spruce)	Northern Europe, Canada, USA	Fairly strong, resistant to splitting, easy to work	General indoor furniture

△ **Table 1.2** Common softwoods

Sources of wood

Wood is a sustainable material. This means that it is naturally replenished – when you use it you can grow some more. It takes about 30 years to grow the quickest-growing softwood tree to a useable size. Hardwood trees grow more slowly, taking up to 100 years to reach a useable size.

Large amounts of softwood are grown in managed forests. In these, new trees are planted to replace each one that is cut down. In the UK we grow about 10 per cent of the softwood we use. Much of the rest is imported from Scandinavian countries.

The Forest Stewardship Council (FSC) logo is used to identify wood from responsibly managed forests.

◁ **Figure 1.5** FSC logo

Conversion

The first step in turning a tree into useable wood is to cut down the tree! Next, the branches are cut off and the bark is removed from the trunk. On the inside of the tree you will see a series of rings – these represent periods of growth.

The trunk is then cut along its length, into roughly sawn boards. This process is known as conversion. The rings from inside the tree will be visible as lines in the boards – this is called the grain. The properties of the wood will vary in different directions, depending upon its grain.

At this stage the wood is often referred to as green timber. This has nothing to do with its colour – it is because the wood contains a lot of moisture. Although green timber is sometimes used for construction projects, normally it is dried out before it is made into useable forms. This is because, as green timber dries, it shrinks. This can cause it to twist, warp and split.

The process of drying the wood is known as seasoning. It is normally done by stacking the rough-sawn boards so that air can circulate easily between them. This can be carried out naturally in the air, but it takes a long time. Often it is carried out in a kiln (see Figure 1.7). This raises the temperature of the air slightly and helps speed up the drying process.

Market forms

Market form refers to the size and shape of the timber that you can buy (see Figure 1.6). After conversion and seasoning, the timber is ready to be machined into the form it will be sold in. This might be carried out using circular saws, band saws and planing machines.

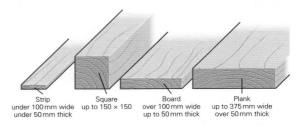

Strip
under 100 mm wide
under 50 mm thick

Square
up to 150 × 150

Board
over 100 mm wide
up to 50 mm thick

Plank
up to 375 mm wide
over 50 mm thick

△ **Figure 1.6** Standard timber sections

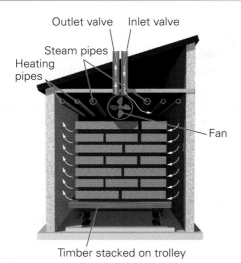

Outlet valve   Inlet valve
Steam pipes
Heating pipes
Fan
Timber stacked on trolley

△ **Figure 1.7** Kiln seasoning timber

Normally the timber is made into a standard size and shape. Rough-sawn timber is often planed to give it a smooth surface. If it is planed on two sides only, it is referred to as planed both sides (PBS). If it is planed on all four sides, it is called planed all round (PAR). Planing makes the wood approximately 3 mm smaller than the sawn size. Planed timber is more expensive than sawn timber. However, it has the advantages of a smooth finish and accurate size (see Figure 1.8).

Some of the timber may be made into different shapes, called mouldings (see Figure 1.9). This is done by machining it using special cutters. Mouldings are often used for decorative purposes, such as skirting boards or the trim around other wooden parts. The wood that is cut away to form the shape of the mouldings is not wasted; it is used in the production of

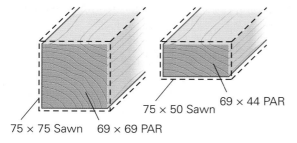

75 × 75 Sawn   69 × 69 PAR
75 × 50 Sawn   69 × 44 PAR

△ **Figure 1.8** Typical planed timber sizes

manufactured boards, which is explained in the following section.

Standard sections

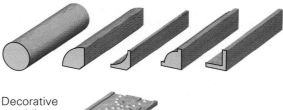

Decorative moulding

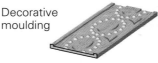

△ **Figure 1.9** Timber mouldings

> ### Key terms
> **Hardwood** – wood obtained from deciduous trees, which lose their leaves in the autumn.
>
> **Softwood** – wood obtained from coniferous trees, which retain their leaves all year round.
>
> **Seasoning** – drying green timber to remove moisture.
>
> **Moulding** – a shaped section machined from timber.

Manufactured boards

Manufactured boards are made from wood. Depending on the type of board, this might be thin sheets of wood, pulp or particles. These are compressed and bonded with adhesive. They have several advantages over solid timber.

- They can be much larger sizes than solid timber planks. Sheets as large as 2440 × 1220 mm are readily available.
- Their properties are not affected by the grain of the wood.
- They are stable products. This means that they will not twist and warp like green timber.
- They are normally less expensive than solid timber.
- They tend to use more of the tree (or even scrap materials from cutting solid timber).

This means that there is less waste, so they can be more environmentally friendly.

Types of manufactured board

Figure 1.10 shows manufactured boards in common use.

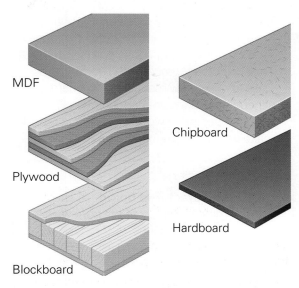

△ **Figure 1.10** Commonly used manufactured boards

Medium density fibreboard

Medium density fibreboard (MDF) is made by squeezing together tiny particles of wood with glue. It has no grain and a very smooth surface. To improve its appearance, it can be covered with a thin strip of timber, known as a veneer (see Figure 1.11). MDF is used to make furniture for indoor use.

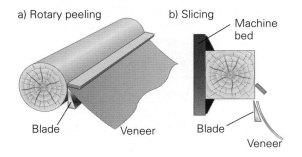

△ **Figure 1.11** Cutting wood veneers

Controlled assessment link

If you are using wood in your Controlled Assessment work, it will be important for you to know its properties, working characteristics and market forms. The student in Figure 5.7 will have needed to consider these things when choosing wood to make his product.

Hardboard

Hardboard is made by squeezing together small wood fibres with glue. It has lower strength than other manufactured boards. Normally, one side of the board is smooth and the other has a rough texture. It is often used in applications where it is normally out of sight, such as drawer bottoms or the back of cupboards.

Chipboard

Chipboard is one of the lowest-cost types of manufactured board. It is made by compressing together small chips of wood with glue. It can be difficult to work with, as the surface is quite rough and it can crumble. It is often covered with a veneer or a thin layer of plastic to improve its appearance. It is often used to make kitchen worktops.

Plywood

Plywood is made by gluing together veneers. Each strip is glued to the previous one with the grain running at 90°. There is always an odd number of veneers. This means that the top and bottom strips run in the same direction. For applications where the appearance of the wood is important, the top and bottom strips are often made from high-quality hardwood.

Blockboard

Blockboard is made by gluing softwood strips side by side. These are then sandwiched between thin strips of wood known as plies. The plies are the visible top and bottom surfaces of the board. The grain of the plies runs at 90° to the softwood strips. It is used for furniture, such as tabletops.

Market forms of manufactured boards

Unlike solid timber, the size of a manufactured board is not limited by the size of the tree it was made from. They are available in a wide range of standard thicknesses (see Table 1.3). Smaller board sizes are made by cutting down the standard board.

Disposal of wood and manufactured boards

There are several ways of disposing of wood products and manufactured boards when they are no longer needed.

○ Furniture made from solid timber is often reused or sold on. Most of the furniture seen on antiques programmes on the television is made from wood.

○ They could be burned to make energy. Trees use the carbon dioxide in the atmosphere to make wood. This means that burning wood is 'carbon neutral' – so long as replacement trees are planted, in the long term it does not increase the amount of carbon dioxide in the atmosphere. Carbon dioxide is one of the gases that causes global warming and can be produced as pollution when other fuels are burned.

○ They may be buried as 'landfill' waste. Wood and manufactured board are biodegradable. This means that they will naturally rot and break down into natural products over time. As such, they do not cause pollution.

○ They could be reprocessed. They might be used to make new manufactured boards, although this does not happen often. They might be put into a wood chipper and used to make wood chippings for use in the garden.

Key terms

Manufactured board – a sheet of material mostly made from waste timber products.

Veneer – a thin strip of wood.

Biodegradable – a material that breaks down naturally over time.

Pollution – contamination of the environment.

1.4 **Metal**

Man has been making items from metal for more than 10,000 years. Some of the earliest items have been found in Asia and Turkey. These include jewellery, spearheads and knives.

Type of board	Board sizes	Standard thicknesses
MDF	2440 × 1220 mm; 2440 × 607 mm; 1220 × 607 mm	3 mm; 6 mm; 9 mm; 12 mm; 16 mm; 18 mm
Plywood	2440 × 1220 mm	4 mm; 6 mm; 9 mm; 12 mm
Blockboard	2440 × 1220 mm	18 mm
Chipboard	2440 × 1220 mm; 1220 × 607 mm	12 mm; 18 mm
Hardboard	2440 × 1220 mm	3 mm; 6 mm

△ **Table 1.3** Standard sizes of manufactured boards

Activities

1. List ten different types of product made from wood that are used in your school. Explain why they were made from wood.

2. Using the internet, find the names of ten different types of softwood and ten different types of hardwood. Find a picture of the appearance of each of these.

3. Prepare a stock list of the wood materials held in your school workshop. This should be in the form of a table and include details such as:

   o the type of timber or manufactured board
   o for timber, whether it is a hardwood or softwood
   o the form
   o the size.

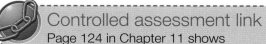

Controlled assessment link

Page 124 in Chapter 11 shows examples of students' Controlled Assessment work using metal. They will have needed to have an understanding of types of metal and their properties in order to decide whether the material was suitable for their product and the processes involved in making it.

Pure metals and alloys

The earliest metal products were made from pure metals such as copper and gold. Pure metals are made from one single element. However, most metals are mixed with other metals to improve their properties. The name for a mixture of two or more pure metals is an alloy. An alloy can also contain other non-metallic elements, such as carbon. The properties of an alloy will depend upon the amounts of the different elements it contains.

Types of metal

There are two families of metals:

o ferrous metals, such as steel, contain iron – see Table 1.4
o non-ferrous metals, such as aluminium and copper, do not contain iron – see Table 1.5.

Ferrous metals

As well as iron, most ferrous metals contain a small amount of carbon. The amount of carbon added depends upon the type of steel and the properties required. For example, high-carbon steel, which is used to make tools and drills, contains 0.7–1.4 per cent carbon. Low-carbon steel, which is also called mild steel, contains less than 0.3 per cent carbon. This is used to make products such as nuts and bolts, and the body panels for cars.

Many ferrous metals are magnetic. One disadvantage of ferrous metals is that they tend to rust. This means that they are often used with protective coatings, such as paint. However, alloying elements can be added to improve their corrosion resistance. For example, stainless steel contains chrome and nickel.

Non-ferrous metals

Non-ferrous metals typically have better corrosion resistance than ferrous metals. They do not contain iron so they do not rust like steel. In general, they are more expensive than ferrous metals.

Metal	Composition	Properties/working characteristics	Uses
Cast iron	Remelted pig iron with additions	Hard skin but brittle soft core; rigid under compression but cannot be bent or forged	Heavy crushing machines, car cylinder blocks, machine parts, vices
Mild steel (low carbon steel)	Alloy of iron and 0.15–0.30% carbon	High tensile strength, ductile, tough, fairly malleable, poor resistance to corrosion; it cannot be hardened due to low carbon content	General purpose, nails, screws, nuts and bolts, plate, sheet, tube, girders, car bodies
Medium-carbon steel	0.30–0.70% carbon	Stronger and harder than mild steel, but less ductile, tough and malleable	Garden tools such as trowels and forks, springs
High-carbon steel	0.70–1.40% carbon	Hardest of the carbon steels; less ductile, tough or malleable	Hammers, chisels, screwdrivers, drills, files, taps and dies
Stainless steel	Alloy of steel with 18% chrome and 8% nickel	Resistant to corrosion, hard, tough; difficult to work	Sinks, dishes, cutlery
High-speed steel	Medium-carbon steel with tungsten, chromium, vanadium	Retains hardness at high temperatures; resistant to high level of frictional heat; can only be ground	Drills, lathe cutting tools
High-tensile steel	Low-carbon steel with nickel and chrome	Extremely hard and tough	Gears, shafts, engine parts, turbine blades

△ **Table 1.4** Common ferrous metals

Metal	Composition	Properties/working characteristics	Uses
Aluminium	Pure metal	Light, soft, ductile, malleable, can be welded, good conductor of heat and electricity, corrosion-resistant, polishes well	Aircraft bodies, saucepans, cooking utensils, packaging, foils, cans, window frames
Duralumin	4% copper, 1% manganese and magnesium	Equivalent strength as mild steel but much lighter, ductile, machines well, becomes harder when worked	Aircraft and vehicle parts
Copper	Pure metal	Malleable, ductile, tough, good conductor of heat/electricity, easily joined, corrosion-resistant; easily soldered	Electrical wire, hot-water tanks, central-heating pipes, printed circuits
Gilding metal	Alloy of 85% copper, 15% zinc	Corrosion-resistant, solders easily, attractive golden colour; can be enamelled	Beaten metalwork, jewellery
Brass	Alloy of 65% copper, 35% zinc	Corrosion-resistant; heat and electrical conductor, easily joined; casts well	Castings, forgings, ornaments, boat fittings
Bronze	Alloy of 90% copper, 10% tin	Tough, hardwearing, corrosion-resistant	Bearings, castings for statues, coins; air, water and steam valves
Lead	Pure metal	Very soft, heaviest common metal, malleable, corrosion-resistant, low melting point, easy to work	Soft solders, roof coverings, protection against x-ray radiation
Tin	Pure metal	Soft, ductile and malleable, low melting point, corrosion-resistant	Soft solders
Tinplate	Steel sheet coated with tin	Mild steel gives it strength, tin coating bends with the steel; non-toxic	Tin cans, light sheet metalwork
Zinc	Pure metal	Poor strength–weight ratio, low melting point, extremely corrosion-resistant, easily worked	Coating (galvanising) steel, e.g. traditional watering cans, buckets and dustbins, intricate die castings

△ **Table 1.5** Common non-ferrous metals

Key terms

Alloy – a metal that is a mixture of two or more pure metals, sometimes with other elements.

Ferrous metal – a metal that contains iron.

Non-ferrous metal – a metal that does not contain iron.

Making metal

Metals are rarely found in their pure form – most are found as an ore, which is rock. This has to be mined from quarries or dug from the ground. This can have a significant effect on the environment in the area of the quarry or mine.

The ore has to be heated to a high temperature in a furnace. This melts the metal in the ore. The liquid metal is then cooled to become solid. The process of pouring liquid metal into a shape is known as casting (see Figure 1.12). If necessary, the metal can then be machined to make it into the finished product.

△ **Figure 1.12** Casting metal

Market forms

The shape and size of the metal is called its form. Metals are made in a range of standard forms (see Figure 1.13). However, as they are used for different purposes, not all metals are made in the full range of forms (see Table 1.6).

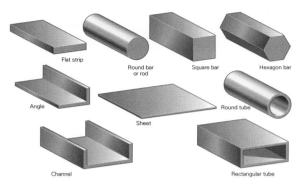

Flat strip

Round bar or rod

Square bar

Hexagon bar

Angle

Sheet

Round tube

Channel

Rectangular tube

△ **Figure 1.13** Standard metal forms

Designers try to use the standard forms and sizes (see Table 1.7), even if it means that they have to change a design slightly. This is because otherwise it may require a lot of time, energy and cost to machine the metal.

Metals are also available as shapes cast to individual designs.

Knowledge link

This is explained in the casting section in Chapter 11.

Disposal of metals

As metal parts are often strong and tough, they frequently last longer than the products that are made from them. Where possible, the individual parts of these products can be reused. For example, scrapyards collect broken-down cars and sell the parts to people who need them. It is normally much cheaper to buy these parts than to buy replacements.

Metal products that have reached the end of their useable life can be recycled. This is done by adding them to the furnace with the metal ore and melting them again.

Metal	Wire	Bar	Flat	Tube	Shaped sections
Mild steel		Round Square Hexagon	Strip Sheet Plate	Round Square Rectangular	Angle Channel Tee H section
Aluminium alloy	0.5–3 mm thick	Round Square Hexagon	Strip Sheet Plate	Round Square Rectangular	Angle Channel Tee
Copper	0.5–3 mm thick	Round Square	Strip Sheet	Round	
Brass	0.5–3 mm thick	Round Square Hexagon	Strip Sheet	Round	Angle

△ **Table 1.6** Metal forms commonly available

Round and square bar	3, 4, 5, 6, 8, 10, 12, 16, 18, 20, 22, 25, 30, 35, 40, 45, 50 mm
Strip	10 × 3, 25 × 3, 50 × 3, 12 × 5, 20 × 5, 50 × 5, 12 × 6, 20 × 6, 50 × 6, 50 × 25, 100 × 50 mm
Sheet	1 m × 1 m, 2 m × 1 m; thickness 0.6, 0.8, 1.0, 1.2, 1.5, 2.0, 2.5, 3.0 mm
Angle	13 × 3 – 3 mm thick, 25 × 25 – 3 mm thick, 25 × 25 – 5 mm thick, 50 × 50 – 6 mm thick

△ **Table 1.7** Typical standard sizes for mild steel

Exam practice questions

1. List ten different types of product made from metal that are used in your home. Identify the type of metal used and the form of metal that the product was made from.

2. Prepare a stock list of the metal forms held in your school workshop. This should be laid out as a table and include details such as:
   ○ the type of metal
   ○ the form
   ○ the size.

Changing the properties of metal

Although a metal product may look like a single lump of material, it is normally made up of millions of tiny metal grains. The grain structure has a big influence on the properties of the metal product.

The nature and size of the grains depend upon the alloy elements in the metal, what temperature the metal has been heated to and how quickly it was cooled down. This means that the properties of metal can be changed by heating and cooling it under controlled conditions. This is known as heat treatment.

Quenching and tempering

Quenching and tempering is a hardening process used with ferrous metals.

Steels with a carbon content of 0.8–1.4 per cent are called high-carbon steels. They are often used for products which need to be very hard, such as cutting tools. The hardness of these steels can be increased by the quenching and tempering process.

Quenching involves heating the steel to a temperature just above its lower critical point (see Figure 1.14). It is left at that temperature for a short time to 'soak'. This allows its structure to change. It is then cooled very quickly by immersing the product in oil or salt water, so that it keeps the hard structure. However, quenching on its own makes the steel brittle, which means that the tools might shatter when used.

Tempering is then used to increase the toughness of the quenched steel and remove some of the excess hardness. This involves heating it to a temperature of 230–300°C and then quenching it again in oil or salt water.

When quenching and tempering is carried out in industry, the steel is heated in a temperature-controlled furnace. It is then transferred by

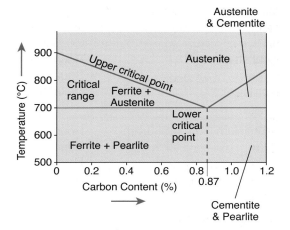

△ **Figure 1.14** Structure of steel at different temperatures

machine to large quenching tanks, which allows precise control over the whole process.

In school workshops, the temperature of the steel often has to be judged by eye. This is done by cleaning the steel with an emery cloth to make it clean and bright, before heating it gently. As the temperature of the steel increases, its colour changes (see Figure 1.15). Once the correct colour appears it is then quenched again.

Colour	Temp. °c	Hardness	Typical uses
Light straw	230	Hardest	Lathe tools, scrapers
Dark straw	245		Drills, taps and dies, punches
Orange/brown	260		Hammer heads, plane irons
Light purple	270		Scissors, knives
Dark purple	280		Saws, chisels, axes
Blue	300	Toughest	Springs, spanners, vice jaws

△ **Figure 1.15** Tempering colours and temperatures

Medium-carbon steels, with 0.4–0.8 per cent carbon, tend to become tougher rather than harder when hardened by each treatment. Steels with less than 0.4 per cent carbon are known as mild steels and cannot be hardened in this way.

Case hardening

Case hardening is a hardening process that is used for mild steels with less than 0.4 per cent carbon (see Figure 1.16). It gives a hard skin that will resist wear.

The case hardening process has two steps: carburising and quenching.

Carburising involves making the surface of a steel product absorb carbon. In industry this is often done by heating the metal in a special gas atmosphere. It can also be done by heating the steel until it is red hot and then dipping it in carbon powder.

The effect of carburising is to change the surface of the mild steel into a high-carbon steel. This can then be hardened by quenching, as described above. As there is only a very thin skin of hard metal, the centre of the steel remains tough and no tempering is needed.

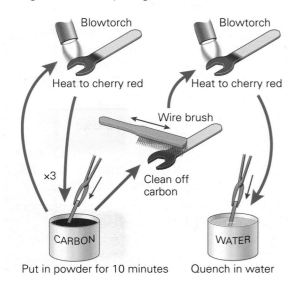

△ **Figure 1.16** Case hardening a mild steel spanner

Normalising

Many metals get harder as work is done to them. This is why some break after repeated bending or hammering. This is known as work hardening (see Figure 1.17).

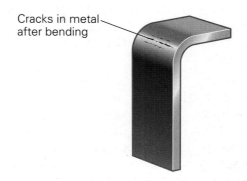

△ **Figure 1.17** Metal failure after work hardening

Normalising is carried out on steel that has become work hardened. It refines the grain structure to make the material tough and ductile. It involves heating steel to just above its upper critical point and then allowing it to cool naturally in still air.

Annealing

Annealing is used to make metal that has been work hardened softer and easier to work. It is used for both ferrous and non-ferrous metals. It involves heating the metal and allowing it to cool slowly.

In industry, annealing is normally carried out using a temperature-controlled furnace. The metal is left to cool very slowly in the furnace after it has been switched off. In the school workshop, annealing can be carried out on a brazing hearth. Firebricks can be used to cover the metal to stop it cooling too quickly.

Annealing ferrous metals

Steel is annealed by heating it to just above its lower critical point. It is then allowed to soak at that temperature for a period of time before being cooled as slowly as possible. This gentle cooling is what makes it different to quenching. This means that the structure can continue to change until it cools down fully.

Annealing non-ferrous metals

The process of annealing for non-ferrous metals depends on which metal is being annealed.

○ Aluminium is heated to 350–400°C and left to cool naturally. Care must be taken to avoid overheating, as it will melt at 660°C.

○ Copper is heated to a dull red heat and then either quenched in water or left to cool in air.

○ Brass is heated to a dull red heat and allowed to cool slowly. It is brittle when red hot and could crack if quenched in water.

For copper and brass, heating them to red hot in air causes the surface to oxidise. This forms a layer of black scale on the surface. This can be cleaned off by putting the metal in a bath of dilute sulphuric acid, which is known as pickling. It can also be rubbed off with damp pumice powder and steel wool.

Key terms

Quenching – cooling metal quickly in oil or water.

Tempering – removing excess hardness and brittleness after hardening.

Soaking – keeping metal at a high temperature for a period of time.

Case hardening – hardening the outer skin of mild steel.

Work hardening – metal becoming harder due to being bent or hammered.

Annealing – softening metal to make it less brittle and easier to work.

1.5 Polymers

Polymers is the correct name for the materials that we normally call plastics. They are typically good electrical and thermal insulators, have good resistance to corrosion and good toughness.

Activities

1. Work harden a piece of copper strip by bending it to a 90° angle. Cut it into two L-shaped pieces. Anneal one of the pieces by heating it to a dull red heat on a brazing hearth and allowing it to cool.

Once it has fully cooled down, mount both pieces and polish them, so that you can look at them under a microscope. Identify any differences in the grain structure of the two pieces.

2. Using the internet, find three examples of products that have been case hardened. Explain why case hardening was used for each of these products rather than using a harder material.

The first synthetic polymer was invented in 1907. It was called Bakelite and was used to make radio casings, children's toys and even jewellery. In the century since then, hundreds of different types of polymer have been invented. They are used in thousands of different products.

Making polymers

The word 'polymer' derives from some Greek words which mean 'many parts'. A polymer is made by attaching together millions of monomers (meaning 'one part') to form a long chain (see Figure 1.18).

Most polymers are made from crude oil (see Figure 1.19). This process is normally carried out by a chemical reaction. The oil has to be put through a complex series of chemical reactions to break it down into monomers and then assemble the polymers.

Other substances are often added to the polymer to change its properties.

○ Plasticisers are added to make the polymer soft and flexible.

○ Pigments are added to make it a particular colour.

○ Fillers, such as wood dust or carbon, are added to increase the bulk. This can make a product cheaper than if it were made out of pure plastic.

○ Flame retardants are added to stop the product burning.

A simple monomer

The structure of the polymer polyethylene

△ **Figure 1.18** Monomers and polymers

△ **Figure 1.19** Drilling for oil

Types of polymer

There are two families of polymer: thermoplastic polymers and thermosetting polymers.

Thermosetting polymers

Thermosetting polymers are also known as thermosets. Table 1.8 on page 20 shows the most common thermosetting polymers.

When a thermoset is made, links form not only between the monomers in the polymer chain but also between different polymer chains. As a result of this, the shape of the thermoset product is fixed permanently – the shape cannot be changed by heating the material again.

Thermosets are typically harder and more rigid than thermoplastics. They are also more resistant to temperature, chemicals and common solvents. However, they tend to be more expensive.

Thermosets are normally sold as chemicals or powder. The ingredients are mixed together when the product is being made.

Thermoplastic polymers

Thermoplastics are the most widely used type of polymer. The word 'plastic' that we often call all polymers is an abbreviation of thermoplastic. Table 1.9 on page 21 shows the common thermoplastic polymers.

The shape of a thermoplastic polymer can be changed when the material is heated. When the material cools, it keeps its new shape. This means that they can be made in standard sheets and re-formed into a wide range of products.

Thermoplastics can also be bought in powder form, so they can be melted to be made into the desired shape.

> ## Controlled assessment link
> The student in Figure 4.1 has used thermosetting polymer in his design. The material's resistance to high temperatures would have been an important consideration when selecting this material for his kettle.

Disposal of polymers

Recycling

Thermoplastics can be recycled. Thermosets cannot be recycled.

Many thermoplastic products are marked with a triangle symbol to show that they can be recycled (see Figure 1.20). The number inside the triangle and the letters indicate which thermoplastic the product is made from. This allows the different types to be sorted so that they can be melted down and made into new products.

Unfortunately, even though they could be, many thermoplastic products are not recycled. Sometimes this is because it may be difficult to separate them from other materials in a product or to sort them. However, often it is because of how people dispose of them.

Common name	Properties/working characteristics	Uses
Urea-formaldehyde	Stiff, hard, brittle, heat-resistant, good electrical insulator, range of colours	White electrical fittings, domestic appliance parts, wood glue
Melamine-formaldehyde	Stiff, hard, strong, range of colours, scratch- and stain-resistant, odourless	Tableware, decorative laminates for work surfaces, electrical insulation
Phenol-formaldehyde	Stiff, hard, strong, brittle, heat-resistant	Dark electrical fittings, saucepan and kettle handles
Epoxy resin	Good chemical and wear resistance, resists heat to 250°C, electrical insulator	Adhesive such as Araldite™ used to bond different materials such as wood, metal and porcelain
Polyester resin	When laminated with glass fibre becomes tough, hard and strong; brittle without reinforcement	GRP boats, chair shells, car bodies

△ **Table 1.8** Common thermosetting polymers

△ **Figure 1.20** Plastics recycling symbols

Waste

At the end of their useful life, thermoset products and many thermoplastic products are thrown away. These may be buried as 'landfill' waste or dumped in the sea. This can be a cause of pollution and damage to the environment. It has been estimated that, each year, more than 100,000 marine animals are killed by plastic bags that have been dumped in the ocean.

 Key terms

Polymer – a material made from a chain of monomers; the correct name for what we often call plastic.

Thermoplastic – a polymer that can be re-formed when heated.

Thermoset – a polymer that cannot change its shape when it is heated.

Common name	Properties/working characteristics	Uses
Low-density polythene	Range of colours, tough, flexible, good electrical insulator and chemical resistance	Washing-up liquid, detergent and squeezy bottles, bin liners, carrier bags
High-density polythene	Range of colours, hard, stiff, good chemical resistance, high impact	Milk crates, bottles, pipes, buckets, bowls
PVC	Stiff, hard, tough, good chemical and weather resistance	Pipes, guttering, roofing sheets, window frames
Polystyrene	Range of colours, stiff, hard, lightweight, safe with food, good water resistance	Disposable plates, cups, fridge linings, model kits, food containers
Expanded polystyrene	Lightweight, absorbs shock, good sound and heat insulator	Sound and heat insulation, protective packaging
Polypropylene	Hard and lightweight, good chemical resistance, can be sterilised, good impact, easily welded together, resistance to work fatigue	Medical equipment, syringes, crates, string, rope, chair shells, containers with integral (built-in) hinges, kitchenware
Nylon	Hard, tough, resilient to wear, self-lubricating, resistant to chemicals and high temperatures	Gear wheels, bearings, curtain-rail fittings, clothing, combs, power-tool cases, hinges
Acrylic	Stiff, hard, clear, durable outdoors, easily machined and polished, good range of colours, excellent impact resistance (glass substitute); does scratch easily	Illuminated signs, aircraft canopies, car rear-light clusters, baths, Perspex™ sheet
ABS	Tough, high-impact strength, lightweight, scratch-resistant, chemical resistance, excellent appearance and finish	Kitchenware, safety helmets, car parts, telephones, food mixers, toys

△ **Table 1.9** Common thermoplastic polymers

Activities

1. Collect examples of thermoplastic products marked with each of the different numbers in the recycling symbol. For each type of plastic, explain why it is a suitable choice for the product it was made into.

2. You have been asked to teach a class of Year 6 pupils the difference between thermosets and thermoplastics. Explain how you will do this, including any examples that you will use. Your lesson must include a practical activity.

1.6 **Composites**

Composite materials are made by combining different types of material. For example, a composite could be made from ceramic and metal. The materials used to make the composite are not bonded together chemically. This means that if you take a section through a composite material, you can still make out the different materials that it is made from (see Figure 1.21).

△ **Figure 1.21** A section through a piece of fibreglass, magnification × 600; the glass fibres are surrounded by a plastic matrix

The reason why composites are important is that they combine the properties of the materials that were used to make them. For example, carbon fibre is very strong and flexible. Polyester resin is rigid. The composite that is created by combining these materials is called carbon reinforced plastic (CRP). It is both strong and rigid.

These combinations of properties can allow the development of new products which were not previously possible. For example, Kevlar™ is a type of polymer. Weight for weight, it is as strong as steel and it is very difficult to cut or break. It is made as fibres, which can be woven into flexible shapes. Ceramic plates are very hard, rigid and brittle. By creating a composite that combines layers of Kevlar™ with ceramic plates, it is possible to make lightweight bullet-proof armour (see Figure 1.22).

△ **Figure 1.22** Composite body armour

Types of composite

There are three basic types of composite: particle composites, laminated composites and stranded composites.

Particle composites

△ **Figure 1.23** Particle composite

Particle composites (see Figure 1.23) are made from small particles of material held in a matrix of a different material.

Cermets are an example of a particle composite. Cermets consist of ceramic particles in a metal matrix. They combine the temperature resistance and hardness of the ceramic with the strength and toughness of the metal. They are often used to make high-quality cutting tools or milling machines and lathes.

Laminated composites

△ **Figure 1.24** Laminated composite

Laminated composites (see Figure 1.24) are made from layers of material. Car windscreens are an example of a laminated composite.

Stranded composites

△ **Figure 1.25** Stranded composite

Stranded composites are made from strands or fibres of a material embedded in a matrix of a different material (see Figure 1.25).

One of the most common stranded composites is fibreglass. This comprises glass fibres in a matrix of polyester resin. Fibreglass is used to make canoes and the hulls of boats. CRP, mentioned on page 22, is another example of a stranded composite. CRP is used to make the body shells of high-performance sports cars and the frames of racing bikes.

Making a composite material

Most composite materials are made as close to the shape of the finished product as possible.

The first step towards making a product from a stranded composite, such as fibreglass, is to make a mould in the shape of the product. There are two types of mould: male and female (see Figure 1.27). The side of the composite that is in contact with the mould will be smooth, the other side will be rough. This characteristic can often be used to identify fibreglass products.

Case study

The windscreens of cars were originally made from glass. They were strong but brittle. Even a minor accident or a stone chip would cause the glass to break into many sharp pieces and splinters, resulting in serious injuries.

In 1903, a French scientist called Edouard Benedictus dropped a glass flask that contained a polymer. The polymer had coated the inside of the glass. He noticed that, although it shattered, it did not break into pieces. This led to the development of a laminated windscreen made from sheets of glass that sandwich a layer of polymer. The windscreen is strong and rigid because of the glass. However, because of the toughness of the polymer, if it breaks it will not break into sharp pieces (see Figure 1.26). Thousands of people have been saved from facial injuries as a result.

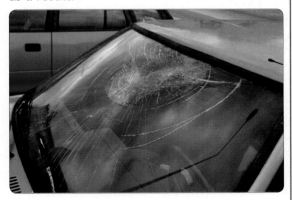

△ **Figure 1.26** Broken windscreen, but still in one piece

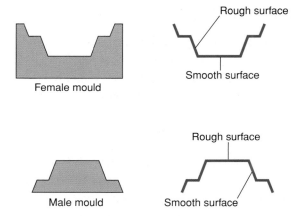

△ **Figure 1.27** Male and female moulds

The mould is covered in a layer of resin. Layers of glass fibre are placed in the mould and pushed by hand into any corners. The fibres are then soaked in resin. This is often painted or sprayed onto it. More layers of glass fibre are added and soaked with resin until the required thickness is reached. The product is then allowed to stand for 24 hours for the resin to set. Once it is hard, any excess material is cut off, any holes needed are drilled and it may be spray-painted.

The whole process is often carried out by hand, which means it is time-consuming and expensive.

Nanocomposites

Nanotechnology is the science of the very small. It is concerned with controlling matter on an atomic scale, to form it into materials with different properties.

Carbon provides a good example of how changing the structure of matter at this scale can change its properties.

○ If the carbon atoms are arranged randomly, it produces soot.
○ In one arrangement, it is graphite. Graphite is a 'soft' form of carbon used in pencils.
○ Arranged another way, it is diamond. This is incredibly hard.
○ Arranged in yet another way, it can form carbon nanotubes. These have the potential to form a material that is hundreds of times stronger than steel.

Nanotechnology is a relatively new area of development. The best ways of making and using these materials are still being determined. However, they are starting to be used in nanocomposites. A nanocomposite is a material where one of the components has dimensions of less than 100 nanometres. To put this into perspective, that is equal to one ten-thousandth of a millimetre.

One nanocomposite that is already being used is glass with a layer of nanomaterial on it. This layer repels dirt and water. This means that it can be used for windows that never need cleaning or for car windscreens that do not need windscreen wipers.

Similarly, textiles with a nanocomposite layer are being developed to make clothing that is resistant to dirt, stains and sweat.

Particle nanocomposites are being developed for food packaging. These provide a better barrier to the atmosphere, which can help food to stay fresh for much longer.

Stranded composites using carbon nanotubes combined with polymers have exceptional strength and low weight. They are being investigated for use in high-performance applications such as aircraft parts.

Waste

The cost and energy needed to separate a composite material into the materials it was made from are high. This means that these materials are normally thrown away at the end of their life rather than being recycled. Most will end up buried in landfill.

Key terms

Composite – a material made by combining two or more dissimilar materials, which remain physically distinct within the body of the composite.

Nanocomposite – a composite material where one or more of the materials combined in it is a nanomaterial, with dimensions of less than 100 nanometres.

Activity

Using the internet, research examples of different composite materials and identify an application that they are used for. For each application, identify what material was used before the composite was invented. What were the advantages and disadvantages of using the composite?

1.7 Smart materials

You have probably seen sunglasses with lenses that become less dark when you go inside. When you go back out into the sunlight they become darker again. The lenses in these glasses are an example of a smart material.

A smart material has a property that reacts to changes in its environment. This change is reversible when the environment changes again. It can also be repeated many times.

The change in the environment could be, for example, light or pressure or temperature. The property that is changed depends upon the material. It might be the shape, the colour, the electrical conductivity, etc.

Calling these materials 'smart materials' is putting them into a category based on the ability of their properties to change. All of these materials could also be categorised based on how they were made, for example as metals or plastics.

Types of smart material
Shape change materials

When a 'normal' metal is stretched or bent beyond its elastic limit, its shape is changed permanently. However, for a shape memory alloy (SMA), if it is then heated to a certain temperature it will return to its original shape. This temperature is known as the transition temperature. This process of bending and straightening can be repeated thousands of times.

One of the most common SMAs is Nitinol, an alloy of nickel and titanium. This has a transition temperature of about 70°C. This means that a deformed Nitinol product can return to its original shape when put in hot water. For thin product or wire made from SMA, this temperature can also be achieved by passing an electrical current through it.

SMA is used in three types of application.

○ Where a response to changes in temperature is needed. These include the triggers for fire alarm systems or controllers for hot water valves in showers.

○ Where movement is needed from an electrical signal. For example, electric door locks, rotary movement and artificial muscles in robot arms, and activating levers (see Figures 1.28–1.30).

○ To allow the repair of 'damaged' products. For example, SMAs are used for spectacle frames. If the user accidentally sits on the frame or bends it, it can be returned to its original shape by being heated to the transition temperature.

Piezoelectric materials

When a voltage is applied to a piezoelectric material, it makes a tiny change in shape. This also works in reverse: a change in shape of the material produces a tiny voltage.

Piezoelectric materials are a vital part of the speakers in miniature headphones and microphones. They are also used as contact sensors.

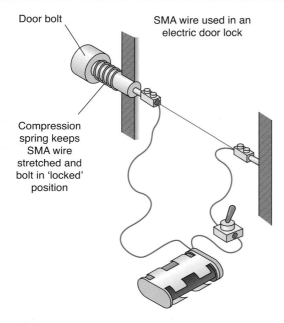

Door bolt

SMA wire used in an electric door lock

Compression spring keeps SMA wire stretched and bolt in 'locked' position

△ **Figure 1.28** Electric door lock

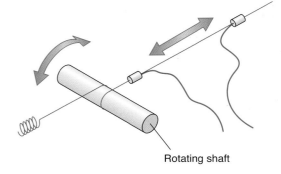

Rotating shaft

△ **Figure 1.29** SMA wire coiled around a shaft, producing rotary movement

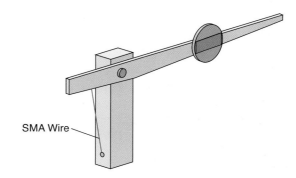

SMA Wire

△ **Figure 1.30** SMA wire used to activate a lever on a model barrier

Case study

Smart skis

When a skier tries to go fast over a rough surface, the skis start to vibrate. This makes them harder to control. Smart skis help to reduce this problem. As the skis vibrate, this changes the size of a piezoelectric material in the ski. This produces an electrical signal which tells a control system that there is vibration.

The control system then sends back an electrical signal, which causes the piezoelectric material to change shape, altering the stiffness of the ski and reducing the vibration. This loop of detection and changing the stiffness is carried out many times per second.

△ **Figure 1.31** Skier

Materials that change electrical characteristics

Quantum tunnelling composite (QTC) is a particle composite. It contains tiny particles of metal in a polymer matrix. Normally, it is an electrical insulator. However, when pressure is applied it becomes an electrical conductor.

QTC can be used for contact sensors and buttons on electrical equipment.

Colour change materials

Thermochromic materials change colour at specific temperatures (see Figure 1.32). They are available in several forms: plastic, ink, dyes for textiles, or paint. The colour change is caused by a pigment within the material.

One of the most common uses of thermochromic materials is for the test strips on the side of batteries (see Figure 1.33). When the strip is pressed at each end, if the battery is in good condition, current flows through a printed resistor under the thermochromic film. This heats the resistor, producing a colour change.

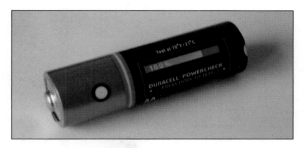

△ **Figure 1.32** Battery showing test strip

Other applications include:

○ plastic strips used as thermometers
○ food packaging that changes colour to show you when the product is cooked to the right temperature
○ colour indicators on cans of drink to show whether the contents are cold enough.

Photochromic materials change colour if the level of light changes. Applications of photochromic materials include:

○ the lenses of sunglasses that become lighter or darker in different light conditions
○ security markers that can be seen only in ultraviolet light
○ colour-change jewellery and nail varnish.

When a voltage is applied to electrochromic glass, it changes from being transparent to being translucent. This means that you can no longer see through it. It can be used in houses or offices to provide privacy without blinds or curtains.

> **Key term**
>
> **Smart material** – a material that changes its properties in response to changes in its environment.

1.8 **Finishing**

Finishing involves changing the surface of a product to improve its properties. There are three main reasons for finishing a product:

○ to protect it from corrosion, weathering or decay

△ **Figure 1.33** Colour change on a mug coated with thermochromic ink

○ to protect it from wear, minor scratches and abrasion

○ to improve the appearance.

In addition, sometimes finishes are used to improve the safety of a product. For example, the handle of an electrician's pliers might be coated in plastic to provide insulation.

The type of finishing used will depend upon the type of material and the reason it is needed.

Finishes for wood

Wood is normally planed and sanded prior to finishing. When varnish or paint is used, if more than one coat of finish is applied the

Activities

1. Choose one type of smart material. Create a list of different applications that it could be used for – this should include existing applications or your own ideas for other products that it could be used for.

2. Write an article for a design magazine explaining how the development of smart materials will affect the work of designers. This should include at least two case studies of products that could be changed to include smart materials.

Finish	Method of application	Properties of the finish	Notes
Oil	Rub into the surface with a cloth	Appearance – adds shine and makes the grain stand out. Provides some protection against moisture	Extra coats can be used to improve shine. Types of oil used include teak oil and Danish oil, which is made mainly from linseed oil
Wax	Rub into the surface with a cloth; buff after it has dried	Appearance – adds shine. Provides some protection against moisture	
French polish	Rubbed in using a 'rubber' (cotton wool wrapped in a cloth)	Appearance – adds shine. Provides some protection against moisture	Mixture of beeswax and methylated spirits
Stain	Cloth or brush	Appearance – changes the colour of the wood	Often sealed after it has dried, to add protection
Sealer	Brush, rub down with glass paper when dry	Appearance – adds shine. Provides good protection against moisture	Often waxed or varnished afterwards
Polyurethane varnish	Brush or spray	Appearance – adds shine and can be used to change the colour of the wood. Provides very good protection against moisture	More than one coat can be applied to increase shine. Available in matt, satin and gloss

△ **Table 1.10** Finishes to wood

Contd

Finish	Method of application	Properties of the finish	Notes
Paint	Brush or spray	Appearance – changes the colour, hides the natural appearance of the wood Provides good protection against moisture	Knots in the wood need to be treated beforehand Primer coat and undercoat may be needed on bare wood

△ **Table 1.10** Finishes to wood

wood is normally rubbed down between each coat (see Table 1.10).

Oil and wax are natural products. Care must be taken when using stain, sealer, varnish and paint as these products can cause pollution when in liquid form.

Finishes for metal

Paint

Paint adds colour to metal. It also gives good protection against corrosion. It is often the cheapest and easiest way of finishing a metal item.

The surface of the metal must be cleaned to remove any oil or grease before painting. Normally, three coats of paint are applied: primer, undercoat and topcoat. The primer is applied to the bare metal. It helps the other coats adhere to the metal. Acrylic paints can be used as a single primer and undercoat.

Hammerite™ is a one-coat cellulose-based paint. It does not need a primer or undercoat. It is available in gloss or hammered finishes and is used for outdoor steelwork.

Dip coating

This involves coating the metal with a layer of plastic. It adds colour to the metal and gives excellent protection. Refrigerator shelves are dip coated.

The metal part to be coated is heated to 180–200°C. It is then dipped into a fluidised bath of polyethylene powder for a few seconds. 'Fluidised' means that air is blown through the

powder to make it behave like a liquid. This helps to ensure that the coating is applied evenly. The polyethylene sticks to the hot metal and it is left to cool.

Galvanising

Galvanising involves dipping a steel product into a bath of molten zinc. The zinc forms a protective coating, which improves the corrosion resistance of the steel.

Electroplating

Electroplating involves coating a metal with a thin layer of another metal. It is used to apply coatings of nickel, zinc, copper, tin or chromium to steel. Nickel and zinc provide good corrosion resistance. Chromium is used to give a shiny appearance. Parts that are chrome plated are normally nickel plated first to improve their corrosion resistance.

It uses a process called electrolysis. The part to be coated is put in a tank containing a chemical solution and an electrical contact. An electrical current is passed through the part and a thin layer of metal slowly builds up on it (see Figure 1.34).

Anodising

Anodising is used for aluminium. It adds colour and gives excellent protection against corrosion. It also makes the surface harder, giving good protection against wear and scratches. Similar to electroplating, the process is carried out in a chemical bath, although no extra metal is used.

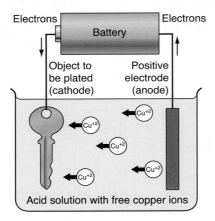

△ **Figure 1.34** Electroplating

Oil blueing

Oil blueing is used with steel. It changes the colour of the metal to blue-black and gives some protection against corrosion.

The steel product is heated to 700°C before being plunged into an oil bath. The oil sticks to the hot metal and is left to cool.

Finishes for plastic

Finishing processes are not normally used with plastics. Plastics are coloured during their manufacturing process. The processes used also give them a very high-quality surface finish.

If there are small scratches and marks on the product these can be removed by polishing with a buffing machine.

Key terms

Finishing – changing the surface of a material in a useful way.

Painting – applying liquid, which dries to form a coating on the surface.

Electroplating – depositing a layer of metal using electrolysis.

Polishing – rubbing or buffing the surface.

Activity

Prepare a strip of wood for finishing. Mark the wood so that it is divided into at least seven equal sections. Leave the first section uncoated. On each of the other sections, apply a different coating. How do the different finishes compare? Rank the finishes in terms of their appearance and how easy (or difficult) they were to prepare.

Controlled assessment link

You will need to know about finishes in your Controlled Assessment work. The examples on pages 153–156 in Chapter 12 show how different finishing techniques have been applied.

chapter 2
Design and market influences

Learning objectives

By the end of this chapter you should have developed a knowledge and understanding of:

○ how to analyse a task, identifying factors that might influence the design
○ how to consider the needs of the client and the user
○ the implications of 'market-pull, technology-push'
○ how to use relevant sources of information to inform decision making when designing
○ product analysis techniques to make critical judgements about the design and manufacture of resistant materials products produced in school or commercially
○ form, function, shape, colour, materials, texture, component parts, decoration and aesthetic appeal to evaluate suitability for purpose
○ ergonomics and anthropometric data
○ aesthetic and functional requirements in relation to cultural diversity
○ the work of successful designers and how to use these influences to inform own designs.

Introduction

The first stage in designing a new product is identifying and 'unpacking' the problem that needs to be solved. There will be lots to consider in solving the problem and much of this involves analysing in detail what you have to do and why. You should keep asking yourself why you have decided to do something and follow a particular course of action. If you constantly analyse and critically evaluate your progress you will have a greater chance of success. You should also consider the advantages of working with others or in a group/team to help you solve the problem. There should be a need to share initial thoughts and views with others to attract as many ideas for development as possible.

To help you start understanding and unpacking the problem in greater depth you need to develop analysis strategies that will help you formulate design ideas and produce design solutions. Understanding what the client and user want from your solution will

help you focus on the areas you need to research in depth to best solve the problem.

This chapter deals with analysing a task and identifying the factors that might influence your design work. It will look at how you explore different pathways for identifying, analysing and understanding what you have to consider. It also focuses on the client and the user, considering their needs and understanding the implication of 'market-pull, technology-push'.

2.1 **Problem analysis**

Why is there a need for a new product? What is the problem you have identified? How do you identify a problem?

'For me design is a question mark. That is how I start every new project' (Gijs Bakker, Droog design, 2007).

Everyone has a different approach when analysing a problem and everyone has a different take on things. It is important to explore all possible avenues.

The process of identifying a problem should begin with a basic understanding of what is needed. The identification of set criteria and a theme is an important aspect in the formulation of thoughts, and provides you with direction and boundaries. Understanding or identifying a problem usually requires a 'go do' approach to make important connections and place them in context. You should try to avoid preconceived ideas of what the outcome may be, but keep an open mind and be prepared to look at lots of possible solutions.

How do you look at the initial anxiety or need and 'unpack' it to determine the problem in more detail? The context or situation for a new product could be as follows.

○ You enjoy the outdoors and in particular camping. At night there is little or no light in the area you pitch the tent. You need a way of lighting up the area that you use to cook, sleep and socialise in (see Figure 2.1).

◁ **Figure 2.1** The solution to camping in the dark: an outdoor lantern

This context or situation could then be 'unpacked' or further explored to create your design brief by considering details such as portability or transporting the device, size, materials, user and user groups, colour scheme, holding the device, a hanging device, renewable energy, etc. This investigation of the initial context or situation will help focus your thoughts and criteria, and guide you in devising a general research plan to analyse specific information (see Figures 2.2–2.4). This will give you a direction

to follow and help to organise your research, ideally focusing only on what is important to your project rather than on generic research.

◁ **Figure 2.2** Portable closing lantern

◁ **Figure 2.3** Wind-up lantern

◁ **Figure 2.4** Solar lantern

Other potential problem areas could be as follows.

○ Many people work at desks in offices. Some desks are cluttered and the worktop space is filled with all sorts of office accessories such as printers, scanners, staplers, sharpeners, other office tools and personal items, such as those shown in Figure 2.5.

△ **Figure 2.5** An untidy desk

○ More meetings are taking place over the internet and it is preferable if a user can see the person they are speaking with. This happens not only in offices but also in everyday households. Investigate the possibility of designing a product that could allow people to see each other over the internet while having a meeting (see Figure 2.6).

△ **Figure 2.6** A web camera

○ The popularity of MP3 players has allowed individuals to download large collections of music to take anywhere at anytime. Often, users want to share their music with others in a social setting (see Figure 2.7).

△ **Figure 2.7** An iPod docking station

How to write your context/problem in a format suitable for examination

You need to try to write a 'situation/identification of problem' that states why you need to look into this area, i.e. economic reasons, material developments, developments in technology, energy conservation, environmental issues, user problems, trends, target group. You should be looking at issues to make a new product or an existing solution better.

You must identify a user group that you will be aiming the product at. The kind of products that people want to use change according to their age, and their expectations change according to the kind of lifestyle they aspire to. The identification of a need is tied up with finding out what people want.

Key term

User group – the people you are aiming your product at.

User group and user refinements

Although many products are mass-produced, it is often the case that the item has been developed in such a way as to give the impression that it is unique to you/designed with you in mind. Despite this, many users will still make adjustments or alterations to the product, changing its appearance. Alterations may appear to be abstract or bizarre, but in fact the user has done this to personalise the product to them, as in Figure 2.8.

△ **Figure 2.9** Teenagers

△ **Figure 2.8** A mobile phone cover

A user group is a group of people who are likely to use the product you are designing. They have different needs, wants and desires from those of other user groups and the general market. Understanding or identifying your user group in more detail will enable you to generate designs more suited to that group and more likely to be successful with them.

Examples of user groups are:

○ teenage boys and girls
○ the elderly
○ visually impaired adults
○ single mothers
○ adults with specific disabilities
○ children aged 4–10.

△ **Figure 2.10** Elderly people

As you should be able to see from the previous examples, it is important that the user group you are designing for is specific and not too wide ranging. By selecting a specific group you will consider their needs and preferences rather than researching and designing in general.

Often a new product may be developed from an existing one, by modifying its aesthetic or functional characteristics to meet changing user needs. This kind of product development often involves redesigning to add value to a product – to improve its performance, function or appeal. Many 'new' products are developed in this way and may use existing technology in a new context or take a different approach to a problem. Sometimes new products are developed to fulfil completely new contexts – in this case a product may be described as innovative.

Once you have identified your user needs and a problem to be solved, you can start to focus/unpack the problem by asking specific questions about the kind of product that you could design and make to solve the problem. You could think about the purpose and potential for the product. How will it benefit your user group? What is the price range of the products your user group purchases? What kinds of materials do the products your user group purchases use? What are current product design trends or styles?

The characteristics of products must also change if they are to fulfil the developing needs of users and sell into a market at a profit. Once the requirements of users are known they can be analysed and problems that give rise to the need for new products identified. Is your user group concerned about the use of renewable materials or renewable energy? How would this affect the price and the requirements of your user group?

The design brief

A design brief is the statement of a problem that explains in greater detail what you are setting out to produce/solve/improve or make better, and why. Developing a design brief should focus on what you want to do, and should develop from your exploration and analysis of user group needs and problems, and from your identification of a potential product that it is feasible for you to make. The design brief needs to be simple and concise, and explain what needs to be done, but it should not include the solution to the problem as at this stage it is unlikely that you will know what your outcome will look like. In other words, it should give you direction but not be so precise and specific that you are not left with any room for imagination, innovation or development.

How to write your design brief in a format suitable for examination

Describe exactly what the problem is and how you are going to try to solve it. Write in full sentences and make links to the user group you have decided to design for. It will always make your design brief look better if you can include images of the user group or client, the 'space' you are designing for. If you can visualise the problem to be solved, this communicates what you are trying to do far more easily than writing lots of words (see Figure 2.11).

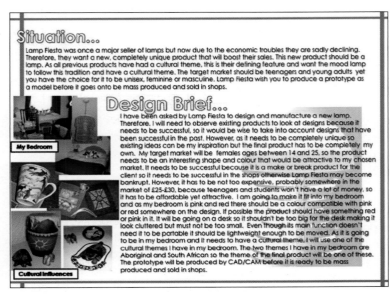

Situation...
Lamp Fiesta was once a major seller of lamps but now due to the economic troubles they are sadly declining. Therefore, they want a new, completely unique product that will boost their sales. This new product should be a lamp. As all previous products have had a cultural theme, this is their defining feature and want the mood lamp to follow this tradition and have a cultural theme. The target market should be teenagers and young adults yet you have the choice for it to be unisex, feminine or masculine. Lamp Fiesta wish you to produce a prototype as a model before it goes onto be mass produced and sold in shops.

My Bedroom

Cultural Influences

Design Brief...
I have been asked by Lamp Fiesta to design and manufacture a new lamp. Therefore, I will need to observe existing products to look at designs because it needs to be successful, so it would be wise to take into account designs that have been successful in the past. However, as it needs to be completely unique so existing ideas can be my inspiration but the final product has to be completely my own. My target market will be females ages between 14 and 25, so the product needs to be an interesting shape and colour that would be attractive to my chosen market. It needs to be successful because it is a make or break product for the client so it needs to be successful in the shops otherwise Lamp Fiesta may become bankrupt. However, it has to be not too expensive, probably somewhere in the market of £25–£30, because teenagers and students won't have a lot of money, so it has to be affordable yet attractive. I am going to make it fit into my bedroom and as my bedroom is pink and red there should be a colour compatible with pink or red somewhere on the design. If possible the product should have something red or pink in it. It will be going on a desk so it shouldn't be too big for the desk making it look cluttered but must not be too small. Even though its main function doesn't need it to be portable it should be lightweight enough to be moved. As it is going to be in my bedroom and it needs to have a cultural theme, I will use one of the cultural themes I have in my bedroom. The two themes I have in my bedroom are Aboriginal and South African so the theme of the final product will be one of these. The prototype will be produced by CAD/CAM before it is ready to be mass produced and sold in shops.

△ **Figure 2.11** Design brief

Discuss how you are going to analyse your problem in more detail. What are you going to research and look at to help you produce a range of design ideas? Are you going to research existing solutions to your problem, or a similar one, to find out more information about how others have solved a similar problem? Could you ask your user group what they think of current solutions on the market and then use this information to help write a detailed design specification that will help you solve the problem with a 'best fit' for their needs?

You could identify the successes, the failures and the problems with existing solutions and, with these identified, you should hopefully produce a product that solves or improves these problems.

Example questions you could ask include:

- What is the need or problem I can solve?
- Who is/are the potential user group(s)?
- How can I solve the need/problem?
- What might the intended product be?
- Where will the product be used?
- How will it be used?
- What benefits will it bring to users?
- Does it have to conform to a standard size?
- Are there standard components that have to be fitted?
- What about aesthetics?
- Does it need to fit any regulations, such as for safety or quality?
- How should the product perform?
- What kinds of materials and processes can I use?
- What is the potential price range?
- Is it something that I can design and make?
- What about developments in technology?
- What about environmental issues?

Task analysis plan

The statement you have written in the design brief does not give all of the information about the problem or how you are going to approach researching the problem. This could be considered a 'plan' of what you are going to do to generate

Key term

Task analysis plan – a diagram that covers the areas you need to consider in order to solve your problem.

solutions to the problem. What you actually need to do is analyse your design brief in more depth, thinking about what you have to do to know more about the problem you are trying to solve.

A task analysis (spider/web diagram) plan covers the areas that you should research and consider if you are going to solve the problem that you face. Your research plan needs to be targeted and relevant, not generic, and it should focus on the problem, product and user needs in order to find out useful information that will help you make decisions about what you intend to design and make. Listed below are some starter points that you could consider using in your task analysis plan:

- existing solutions
- user
- materials
- aesthetics
- design
- form
- function
- environmental issues
- cost
- components
- construction technology
- price ranges
- economics
- safety
- size
- ergonomics
- anthropometrics
- industrial practices and processes
- finish, etc.

You could also comment on the following.

Manufacture processes – what processes may you need to know about in order for your design to be manufactured? Are you intending to solve the problem and manufacture your final designs using any CAD or CAM?

Existing solutions – what products are already available on the market? What are the features of these products that make them good or bad?

Anthropometrics – these are the measurements of the average person/man/woman/baby, etc. that help designers decide what size to design products and make them more ergonomic.

Ergonomics – this describes how people interact with products. If a product is comfortable it could be described as being ergonomic. It is linked to anthropometrics and size.

Environmental issues – comment on the environmental issues you could consider: use of recycled materials, reducing the amount of materials your product uses, design for disassembly, using renewable energy sources, solar panels, wind-up power, wind power, etc. This could also link to manufacture,

e.g. where a product is manufactured will affect how environmentally friendly it is if it has to be shipped to a different country after manufacture.

You could also use an analysis strategy to help you do this, such as the 5Ws:

- Who will use the product?
- Where will the product be used?
- Why is the product needed?
- What precisely does the product have to do?
- When will the product be used?

How to present your task analysis plan in a format suitable for examination

You should produce a web analysis/spider diagram based around your chosen project at the centre. You should then think of all the points you need to investigate further to help you solve the problem. Try to explain each of the points, why you need to investigate and research them, and how they will help you solve the problem (see Figure 2.12).

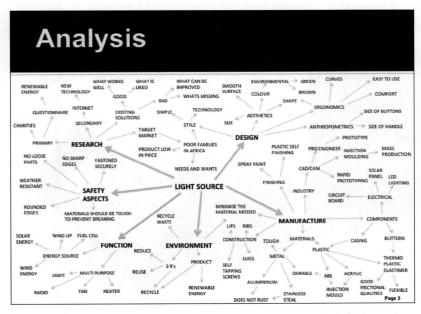

△ **Figure 2.12** Example analysis web for a wind-up camping lantern

2.2 **Market-pull, technology-push**

You should try to understand whether the problem you are attempting to solve fits into one of these areas. Market-pull means business or users have a need for a product and technology develops to fill that need. Technology-push means new technology has been developed and the 'need' or 'users' must be created.

Market-pull

Market-pull in design terms usually means that users want a design or product to be relaunched or redeveloped to meet updated needs. One example of a market-pull product is the Mini (Figure 2.13). The Mini is a small car that was designed by Sir Alec Issigonis and made by the British Motor Company from 1959 until 2000. The original is considered a British icon of the 1960s and its design influenced a generation of car makers. The vehicle is in some ways considered the British equivalent of its German contemporary, the Volkswagen Beetle (another example of a market-pull product). In 1999 the Mini was voted the second most influential car of the twentieth century. The Mini has since been developed by BMW and was relaunched incorporating new technology to match the needs of current users.

△ **Figure 2.13** The new-look Mini

Technology-push

Technology-push is when new technology is developed and designers investigate ways in which they can embrace the technology for different uses and products. An example of a company at the forefront of technology-push is Apple. Products such as the iPod (Figure 2.14) and the iPad have been developed thanks to new technological developments. Before the iPod was launched in 2001, users had the Walkman, Mini-Discman and Discman.

The new technology of the iPod allowed users to download music from a server or computer onto a solid-state hard drive (one that has no moving parts). This allowed for thousands of songs to be stored rather than just a single CD or cassette tape as previously. Further music could be added just by downloading to the device. The iPod also used a rechargeable battery, rather than replaceable batteries. Further iterations of the iPod have since been launched when the technology has developed further to include colour screens, digital cameras, video and greater storage in a reduced size. All of this has been thanks to the technology-push and electronic microprocessors reducing in cost and size and increasing in power.

The iPad is a great example of a product developed through technology-push as users didn't really know they wanted one until it was launched. It is now changing the way we think about computing. The

△ **Figure 2.14** Technology-push: the iPod

iPad sold 2 million units in the USA alone when it was launched in 2010 and has sold 15 million units worldwide in less than a year.

Key terms

Market pull – business or users have a need for a product and technology develops to fill the need.

Technology push – new technology is developed and designers investigate ways in which to embrace the technology for different users and products.

2.3 Research and analysis

Once you have written your design brief and formulated your task analysis plan you can really start researching your project. In this phase you will investigate, analyse and gather information about what your user group would like. You should ask your user group questions about what their needs are. You should look at existing solutions on the market to see where your product would fit, and gain valuable information from them to help improve your designs.

How to find out what your user group wants

The most popular ways of finding out what your user group wants would be to design a questionnaire or conduct a user interview. The key to successful research is to ask the right questions. If your questions are not thought through then the answers will not give you information that will help you to generate design solutions to match your user group's needs. This could be referred as 'garbage in, garbage out'.

You need to establish exactly what your user group wants the product to do and any particular features they would like the product to have. You may also want to ask them what aesthetic qualities they would like the product to have. The design of a questionnaire or user interview is critical in

order to get the kinds of answers that allow design decisions to be made. You should always try to test a questionnaire or interview before using it. In general, shorter questionnaires or interviews are usually better than long ones as you have more chance of people completing them. You will also use your questionnaire or interview later in your project to help guide the writing of your specification – this is very important.

How to present this information in a format suitable for examination

Conducting an in-depth interview with your user group will give you valuable information and insight into their needs. Think carefully about the questions you will ask and record the responses from each interview. It would also be beneficial for you to record, in some way, the interview taking place. This could be done through a photograph of you conducting the interview or could even be recorded on a video camera/mobile phone. The responses then need to be presented in a format that makes the information accessible.

You should aim to ask 15–20 questions, showing your results either in graph or chart format or through typing the questions and responses onto a document to present the information (see Figure 2.15). If you use a video recording you could insert and embed this into a document. It is recommended that you use IT software to aid your presentation of this information.

As mentioned earlier, the wording of the questions is vital. The questions should be:

o relevant – include only questions that target the information required
o clear – avoid long words, jargon and technical terms; questions must be easy to understand
o inoffensive – take care with questions about age, social class, salary, ethnicity, so as not to cause offence
o brief – short questions of fewer than 20 words

Interview

What is your first impression of the product, just by looking at it?
• It is sleek and is well finished. The corners are rounded, which I like because it looks more professional.
• It is easy to use as there is not a lot of buttons, therefore it is not confusing.
• Also it is easy to pack away in a bag or a suitcase. However it can be quite stiff to actually bend the product.

What do you like about the product?
• I like the fact that you can listen to the music on your iPod externally.
• Also it charges my iPod at the same time, therefore I can listen to my music without turning it off to charge it up.
• I like the idea of the two covers that cover the speakers, as it keeps dust away from them when not using the product.

What do you not like about the product?
• It hasn't got a very exciting and unique design
• I would buy it for the function rather than for the style of the docking station
• The speakers are a bit small, as a result the music cannot produce the best sound quality.

Is the sound quality good? Why do you think this?
• The sound quality is okay but there are better iPod docking stations with better quality speakers for the same price on the market.
• As a result of the quality of the sound I think it is due to the result of the speakers being to small.
• However overall the sound quality is quite good for the simplicity of the product.

How much did your current iPod docking station cost?
• I paid in the region of £20, however no more!

Do you think this is cheap or expensive?
• I think this is a reasonable price as it is quite cheap compared to the high technology iPod docking stations which you see in the region of £90+.

What would you change about this product?
• I would make it more unique, give it a feature or a different design so it stands out compared to the other competition.
• The unique point might make the docking station more sellable, therefore more wanted.
• It just looks like any other iPod docking station, nothing that stands out from the other docking stations.

Do you think the chosen use of material is good? Would you chose another material?
• The material is good because it is durable, I think this is a good quality because most teenagers like myself drop things easily. I think the material does everything it is designed to do.
• I wouldn't change the material because any other material in my opinion wouldn't give a better result as the plastic currently does.

Do you think it does everything it is designed to do?
• Yes I think it does everything it is designed to do. However I think it could be updated more, for instance make it more modern.

If you had to add another feature to this product what would it be?
• A travel cover because when I go on holiday the iPod docking station wont get scratched or damaged on long journeys.
• A clock with and alarm that preferably lit up so you could see it in the dark.
• It should come with rechargeable batteries so it would be easier instead of buying batteries all the time, however still keep the mains electrical source.

Would you buy this product?
• I would consider to buy this product however there may be better iPod docking stations for the same price.

△ **Figure 2.15** Example of a questionnaire and results

- precise – each question should tackle one topic at a time
- impartial – avoid 'leading' questions that influence the answer.

Possible questions could be based around environmental issues, renewable energy, age group, colour, finish, type of style user group would prefer, comfort, price or costing – what the user group are prepared to pay for the product you are designing, size of product, packaging, presentation, logo/company name or information – what company brands do you associate with quality or 'coolness'? Does this affect your judgement?

Ergonomics and anthropometrics

People come in all shapes and sizes so you need to take these physical characteristics into account whenever you design anything that someone will use, from something as simple as a pencil to something as complex as a chair.

Anthropometrics is the study of human measurements and the data are used by designers to make products more ergonomic. A designer needs to make sure that the products they design are the right size for the user group and therefore comfortable to use – more ergonomic. Designers have access to drawings that have been created by taking the measurements of thousands of people to find average sizes (see Figure 2.16). People who fall outside of the average, i.e. are very short or very tall, are referred to as either the 5th percentile or the 95th percentile.

Key terms

Ergonomics – the way in which products interact with people.

Anthropometrics – study of human measurements.

How to look at existing solutions

If you investigate existing solutions or products that do a similar job to the product you are designing you will find lots of really useful information. The best way to understand a product is to take it apart and analyse it, recording your stages of disassembly. However, you may find it difficult to get hold of lots of examples of the product you are designing, or even to be able to disassemble the product, so you should have a mix of primary and secondary existing solutions.

Primary existing solutions are when you can hold the object in your hands and investigate and analyse it. This is a kinaesthetic (hands-on/handling the product) analysis and investigation as you can look at all aspects of the solution to the problem, focusing on specific areas such as size, weight, texture, finish, temperature, the key areas of the design and your emotional response to the product. You can, of course, see the product from every angle, including the bottom and back of the product.

Secondary existing solutions are when you get images, usually from the internet or magazines, that others have taken. It is secondary research as someone else has already photographed the product and you are analysing what you can see. This is a visual analysis, focusing mainly on aesthetic qualities.

You should investigate and analyse all details of the solutions/products and you could consider the following areas: materials, ergonomics, anthropometrics, aesthetics, finish, colour, shape, form, weight, common features across the existing solutions, economics, environmental considerations, industrial practices (how has it been made, safety, construction), how parts fit together (split lines – why?), internal structure (ribs, webs, bosses and lugs).

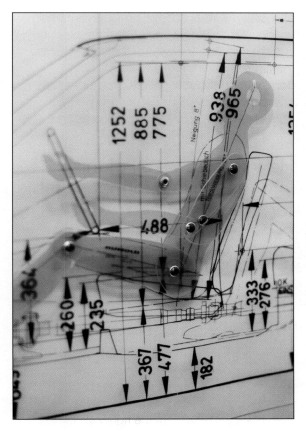

△ **Figure 2.16** Drawing of anthropometric data

Ergonomics is how the measurements of people (anthropometrics) are used to make a product fit or 'work' with a person in an improved way. A chair could be said to be more ergonomic if it is more comfortable to sit on or in. A product may be more ergonomic if it fits your hand to be more comfortable, e.g. a Sky remote control is considered to be an excellent example of an ergonomic product. When considering ergonomics of existing products, you could ask the following questions: What is it that has been aimed for with the product? What measurements have the company/designer had to consider? Who is the user group that the existing solution should accommodate?

ACCESS FM

Many people use the acronym ACCESS FM to help them remember the key areas of initial product analysis and evaluation.

Aesthetics – how it should look, form, shape, colour, texture, finish, decoration, decals

Cost – what is the price range your product will fit into?

Customer – who is your product for? Who is the user? Age? Gender? Likes? Styles? Needs?

Environment – where will the product live or be used? What impact does this have on the design?

Size – what size should your design be?

Safety – what safety considerations are there?

Function – what will or could the product do? Any special features?

Materials – what materials could you use?

Cultural diversity

You could also consider cultural diversity when conducting your analysis of existing solutions or writing your design specification. Many cultures have important traditions that form part of their identity. How do products affect the quality of lives within different cultures? Many cultures use and maintain traditional skills and local knowledge, and these can have an impact on the design of products.

You could consider the responses and values of users from different backgrounds or cultures to existing solutions, and look at the impact of different cultures on existing solutions and how this may have affected the design. Cultural diversity is also the way people behave and relate to each other. It is about the way people live, their beliefs and their aspirations.

We live in a global society and you should consider yourself a citizen of the world rather than just an inhabitant of this island. You need to be aware of the ways that this can affect the designing of products. Are there social issues associated with economic development and employment? Think about where the product is manufactured, the cost of the components, materials, where the raw materials come from, use of labour and workforce (does the company employ locals or bring in workers from elsewhere?), pay and conditions, and transportation of the finished product.

How to present all of this information in a format suitable for examination

There are many ways to present and communicate the information you discover. You could complete all of your analysis and investigation of primary existing solutions through the use of a video camera. You could set up a video camera to record you while you analyse the product, stating the details you are finding out by holding the product. Alternatively, you could photograph the primary solutions from multiple angles and then insert these images onto a document with annotated analysis points around each of the images relating to your findings (Figure 2.17). You should produce your secondary existing solutions research using a similar method (Figure 2.18).

This existing solutions research analysis should provide you with a good understanding of the problem, how others have solved a similar design brief and the desired aesthetic, functional and performance requirements of the product you intend to design and make. This, combined with the results from your user interview or questionnaire, will help you to write your design specification.

Work of designers

Another great starting point for design inspiration is to consider successful designers and their work output. Look at their work and then try to imagine where they got their inspiration. A great example of two successful designers who reference each other's work is the German designer for Braun, Dieter Rams, and the chief designer for Apple, Jonathan Ive. They cite each other's work as an inspiration for their design work.

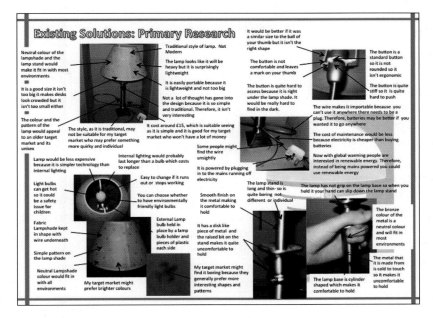

△ **Figure 2.17** Example of primary existing solutions

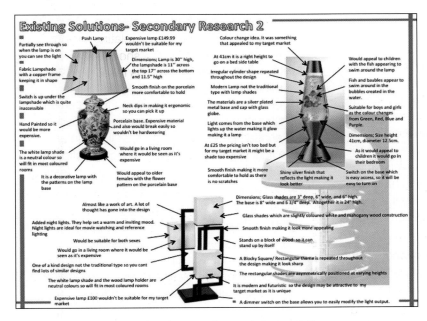

△ **Figure 2.18** Example of secondary existing solutions

2.4 **Product specification**

A design specification is a list of requirements that a product must meet. The design specification is written by producing a summary of all of the most important information you have analysed during your research.

A design specification is the detailed information that guides a designer's thinking about what is to be designed. It is used to help generate, test and evaluate design ideas, and to help develop a manufacturing specification.

Your design specification needs to take into account designing for manufacture – where considerations for design should include the purpose, function, aesthetic and performance requirements of the product; materials, components or systems; market and user requirements; environmental concerns; energy implications; any values issues that may influence your design ideas and considerations about manufacturing processes, technology, scale of production; quality and safety issues; time, resource and cost constraints.

Your design specification should include measurable characteristics that will help you design with manufacture in mind. It needs to include enough detail to develop feasible design ideas that you could possibly make, but leave room for creativity. Your specification should be listed as bullet points, in sub-sections, and should number 15–30 clear, relevant points. Each point (ideally) should have some explanation or rationale as to why it is important – don't just write a very short bullet point, but rather ensure that you explain why.

Consider Figure 2.19. A poor example would be 'It must have no sharp edges'; a better example of the same statement would be 'I must consider designing ideas without sharp edges as the user of the lantern may harm their hand when holding

or repositioning the lantern inside the tent.' The second example goes into the detail of why the product should not have any sharp edges, and it is this additional information that achieves a higher grade.

Use the following checklist to help develop your product design specification. These could also be titles of sub-sections when writing your specification:

o the product's purpose, function and aesthetics
o user requirements and needs
o the expected performance requirements of the product, materials and components
o the kinds of processes, technology and scale of production you may use
o any value issues that may influence your design, such as cultural, social, sustainable or environmental concerns
o the use of renewable energy or materials
o any quality control and safety procedures that will constrain your design
o time, resource and cost constraints you will have to meet.

Your design specification should guide all your design thinking and provide you with a starting point for generating design ideas. Your specification can change during the course of a project and develop as research is carried out, often starting as an outline specification until the final design or manufacturing specification is reached. This is used as a check when testing and evaluating design ideas, and provides information about the solution that can help to monitor its quality of design.

The design specification is an essential document that sets up the criteria for the design and development of your product. Specification criteria can also be used later on to guide your thinking when developing a manufacturing specification.

△ **Figure 2.19** Example of a design specification for a camping lantern

How to present this information in a format suitable for examination

You should list the points of your design specification in a document. This could be a hand-written list or typed onto an electronic document. You should try to organise your list into themes or sub-sections based around your research findings, as in Figure 2.20.

△ **Figure 2.20** Example of a design specification with sub-section headings

Learning objectives

By the end of this chapter you should have developed a knowledge and understanding of:

- what is meant by 'product life cycle'
- why certain materials were chosen and used
- what is meant by planned obsolescence
- what are the 6Rs
- what we can do to ensure that the eventual disposal of product/materials is as eco-friendly as possible.

Introduction

You should consider the choices of materials and processes, and how they would impact on the life cycle of your product and its sustainability.

3.1 The 6Rs

The aim of this section is to develop your knowledge and understanding of sustainability of design, environmental concerns and the life cycle of your product. You could look at how design and technology have evolved through analysis of products from the past and present. You should consider how future designs and your product might impact on the world in which we live.

Recycle

Recycling is what we do with the objects we use in our daily lives. It is the conversion of waste products into new materials, to extend the life and usefulness of a product, item or object that seems to have no more purpose or use once it has been finished with or used for its initial purpose. Recycling means reusing a product, but sometimes, before a product can be reused, it will need to undergo processing or treatment.

There are three main types of recycling, depending on the materials used for the product or how the product needs to be recycled:

- primary recycling
- secondary or physical recycling
- tertiary or chemical recycling.

Primary recycling

Primary recycling is a form of using products second hand. This means that the product is simply being used again. The product can be electrical, mechanical, product-based or clothing. Charity shops are a great place to find second-hand products that are recycled products (giving them a new lease of life). Giving products to friends or family, advertising them in a supermarket, the local paper or a national magazine (e.g. *Autotrader*) or selling them using the internet on a site such as eBay are all ways of primary recycling.

Secondary or physical recycling

Secondary or physical recycling is the process in which waste materials are recycled into different types of product. An example of this is the REEE chair made from parts of computer games consoles (see Figure 3.1). Tarpaulins from the sides of lorries and transport wagons are also now being recycled to make courier bags with a difference.

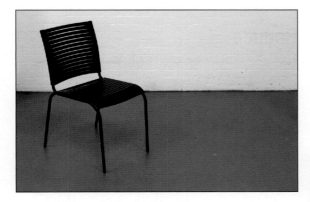

△ **Figure 3.1** The REEE chair, made from parts of computer games consoles

The change the product will go through depends on the main material from which it is made. Packaging used for food is often difficult to recycle. However, biodegradable packaging has been developed and materials such as potato starch waste, corn starch and even biodegradable bubble wrap and films are now being used. Biodegradable or compostable packaging (see Figure 3.2) is preferable to recyclable packaging because recyclable packaging still requires external energy to bring about the recycling process.

△ **Figure 3.2** Good for the environment: biodegradable packaging

Tertiary or chemical recycling

Products are broken down and reformulated – for example, plastic bottles can be recycled into fibres and then respun into polyester to make fleece fabric used for coats and blankets. Car tyres can be reused to make numerous products, such as computer mouse mats. Video cassette tapes are reworked into pencils, as are plastic vending cups and denim (see Figure 3.3). Some glass bottles are used for road surfaces.

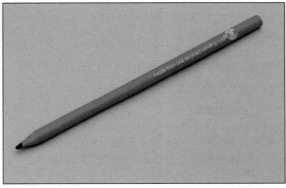

△ **Figure 3.3** First it was a cup, now it's a pencil

Why recycle?

Everything we dispose of goes somewhere, although once the container or bag of rubbish is out of our hands and out of our houses we forget it instantly. Our consumer lifestyle is rapidly filling up rubbish dumps all over the world; as this happens, our concerns for the environment grow.

When designing and making a new product, designers and manufacturers need to consider how it can be recycled at the end of its lifespan. End-of-life disposal is how we dispose of redundant products and their packaging in a safe and environmentally friendly way. All products and packaging are now labelled specifically to help consumers when they come to dispose of them (see Figure 3.4).

Reuse
Products that can be reused for the same purpose or a new purpose

Products that are designed to be reused result in less waste, which leads to conservation of materials and resources. Many places around the UK collect unwanted products or repair them for redistribution for the same or a similar end use. Some may be shipped to another country for distribution and use – for instance, old mobile phones for Africa, old bicycles sent to India.

Products that can be adapted for an alternative use

Some local areas have set up their own websites and organisations for the reuse of unwanted items, involving groups of people who actively aim to adapt existing products for alternative uses. This idea has also been developed on a national level, with organisations such as Freecycle. Freecycle groups match people who have things they want to get rid of with people who can use them. Their goal is to keep useable items out of landfill. By using what we already have on this earth, we reduce consumerism, manufacture fewer goods and lessen the impact on the planet. Another benefit of using Freecycle is that it encourages people to get rid of junk that they no longer need and promotes community involvement in the process.

Reduce

The design of a new product goes through a variety of stages, from the first idea through to its eventual decline, where it may be discontinued or disposed of. This is often referred to as the life cycle of a product. You should consider the impact of a product on society and the environment as a whole. Questions you might ask are:

○ Where does the raw material come from? Where is it processed and how is it made?
○ How does it get from its point of origin to the processing plant? How much transportation or fuel (air miles) does it use? How much do you think that costs or adds to the selling price?
○ What is the intended use of the product? How will it be used by the user group?
○ Could the amount of material used be reduced?
○ How can the product be recycled? Is it environmentally friendly? How can the product be disposed of? Is it recyclable or biodegradable?
○ How much waste do you think is created during the manufacture of the product?

Glass

Please put this in a bottle bank

Aluminium

Recyclable aluminium

Steel

Recyclable steel

Mobius Loop

This is capable of being recycled

Plastics

PETE
Polyethylene terepthalate

HDPE
High-density polyethylene

V
PVC

LDPE
Low-density polyethylene

PP
Polyethylene

PS
Polystyrene

OTHER
All other resins and multi-materials

△ **Figure 3.4** Signs of the times

Key term

Product life cycle – the stages through which a product goes, from initial concept to eventual decline

Controlled assessment link

You will need to consider sustainability of design in your Controlled Assessment work. The student in Figure 2.4 on page 32 has used solar energy as an alternative energy source for his lantern design.

Energy and waste in the production process

The consumption of non-renewable sources of energy such as coal, oil and natural gas is causing an energy crisis. You may have noticed how petrol prices and heating bills at home continue to go up. Non-renewable means that these resources will eventually run out. Non-renewable sources of energy can be divided into two types: fossil fuels and nuclear fuel.

Fossil fuels are found within the rocks of the earth's surface. They are called fossil fuels because they are thought to have been formed many millions of years ago by geological processes acting on dead animals and plants, just like fossils. Coal, oil and natural gas are fossil fuels. Because they took millions of years to form, once they are used up they cannot be replaced – they are non-renewable.

It is thought that the current resources of oil under the North Sea will last about another 20 years, and the world's resource will last for about 70 years unless we do something about our consumption. Transporting oil around the world can produce oil slicks, pollute beaches and harm wildlife. Using non-renewable resources adds to the pollution problem, as products made from oil take a long time to break down in the environment.

Alternative energy sources that are considered environmentally friendly and non-polluting are those generated from the natural sources described below.

Wind

This involves harnessing the power of the wind through turbines. Wind energy can be used to turn turbines that are used to store energy. The advantages of wind power is that the wind is free, people who are not on the national grid can use wind turbines to create their own energy, and they do not produce any greenhouse gases. The disadvantages are that many people think they are an eyesore, they are noisy, and if there is no wind then they are useless.

△ **Figure 3.5** Wind turbines

Solar

Solar energy involves harnessing the power of the sun through solar panels and solar radiators. Energy from the sun is converted to electricity and its storage until it is needed to power a device. Advantages of solar energy are that the sun is free, it will last for ever and the energy can be obtained and used in places where it is difficult to access the national grid. Solar energy is a useful resource. Disadvantages include the fact that it is expensive to set up systems to obtain it, they can function only when it is sunny, and large areas of land are required to capture vast amounts. Solar power is very popular and useful for powering small energy-saving devices such as solar lights, signs and chargers.

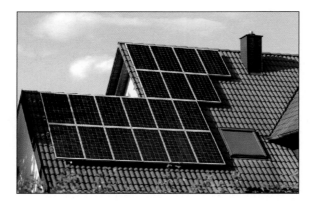

△ **Figure 3.6** Solar panels

Geothermal

This harnesses the thermal energy stored in the earth. The earth's geothermal energy originates from the formation of the planet, from radioactive decay of minerals, from volcanic activity and from solar energy absorbed at the surface. From hot springs, geothermal energy has been used for bathing since early times, but it is now better known for electricity generation. Geothermal power is cost effective, reliable, sustainable and environmentally friendly

△ **Figure 3.7** Steam rising from a geothermal power station

Hydro

This involves harnessing the power of water (hydropower, hydraulic power or water power) through the force or energy of moving water. Before the widespread availability of commercial electric power, hydropower was used for irrigation and operation of various machines, such as watermills.

The water wheel has been around for a very long time. A wheel in a river is turned by water flowing over it, and the wheel turns gears and pulleys to produce movement. Another form of hydro power is producing electricity from water under pressure. An example of this is a dam where large quantities of water flow through turbines to produce energy. Advantages of hydro electricity are that once the dam is built there is a constant supply of electricity and the lake formed by the dam can be used as a leisure facility. A disadvantage is that such schemes must be built to a very high standard and this can be expensive.

△ **Figure 3.8** Water wheel

Tidal/wave

Also called tidal energy, tidal power is a form of hydropower that converts the energy of tides into electricity or other useful forms of power.

△ **Figure 3.9** Tidal energy generators

Kinetic power

Kinetic energy uses movement to generate power. This is very useful in small products such as kinetic watches or wind-up radios, in which energy is generated by human movement. The advantages are that it can be used in remote areas, can be re-obtained and is free. Among its disadvantages are that it can be tiring to generate and can be used to power only small items.

Controlled assessment link
The student in Figure 2.3 on page 32 has used kinetic energy to power his wind-up lantern

Material waste

Waste management is a growing problem, in particular materials used in packaging. Much of this packaging can now be recycled (cardboard and some plastics). However, it is important to consider reducing the amount of material used and wasted in the manufacture of both a product and its subsequent packaging. You can, of course, do your bit towards reducing material waste by simply reusing carrier bags or when buying products not asking for a carrier bag. In the supermarket you could pick fresh fruit and vegetables that are still loose rather than prepackaged.

Manufacturers now have to follow guidelines on how to get rid of their waste effluent. A great example of a manufacturer having to commit to looking at its material waste is Tetra Pak. For many years the Tetra Pak cartons for fruit juices and milk (see Figure 3.10) could not be recycled until, following government legislation, the company was made to investigate ways to do this. Tetra Pak developed a way to break down its cartons and now these can be recycled. The Envirostick was the first pen to be recycled from a Tetra Pak product.

△ **Figure 3.10** Tetra Pak juice carton

◁ **Figure** 3.11 Recycling logo

Built-in obsolescence

Built-in, or planned, obsolescence is where a product has been designed to last for a set period or length of time – the functions of the product have been designed by the manufacturer to fail after a certain time limit. Planned obsolescence is the practice of deliberately shortening the life of products to stimulate sales. Why do you think a manufacturer might do this? Once a product fails or is of no further use because it doesn't work or is out of date, the consumer is under pressure to purchase again. This built-in obsolescence can be found in many wide-ranging products, from vehicles to light bulbs to batteries to computers, from items of clothing to food 'use by' or 'best before' dates (although in many cases this is because the food will start to rot).

It could be stated that there are three main types of obsolescence:

○ function
○ quality
○ desirability.

Function refers to a situation in which an existing product becomes outmoded when the new, better-functioning product is introduced to the market. Quality refers to a situation in which a product is designed to break down or wear out at a given time, usually in a future not too distant. Desirability refers to the situation in which a product that is still sound in terms of quality or performance becomes 'worn out' in our minds because of fashion or other changes that make it seem less desirable.

Manufacturers can invest money to make the product obsolete more quickly by building it with cheaper components, which speeds up this planned obsolescence. Generally speaking, electronic products tend to have limited lives. Think about how much a modern PC or laptop costs. How can one manufacturer make the product so much cheaper than others yet some still cost the same price? How long do these PCs or laptops then last before they become outdated or break?

Key term

Obsolescence – when a product becomes outmoded or out of date.

Refuse

The processing, manufacturing, packaging and transportation of products use huge amounts of energy and create lots of waste. You should look at the sustainability of a product from an environmental and social viewpoint. Ideally,

products' method of manufacture should cause little or no harm to the environment. Sometimes a choice between the required performance of the product and the impact of its manufacture on the environment has to be considered and debated. You could debate whether the product is really necessary. Do we need more than 100 different designs for a toilet brush? Could the product be made from natural sources rather than unnecessarily from man-made materials? Are there toxic chemicals used in the product? Has the product been manufactured ethically (socially and morally) and in compliance with safety regulations? Consider the packaging of the product. What has been used and what are the transport distances (air or shipping miles) and costs? You may have heard of 'food miles' and changed your buying habits. What about 'product miles'?

Repair

For the past couple of decades we have lived in what could be termed 'a throwaway society', meaning it is quicker and easier to throw something away than to repair it. Think about your parents or grandparents and how they solve these issues. Do they try to fix things rather than throw them away? Certainly the 'older' generation will attempt to repair products before consigning them to the rubbish bin. You can repair some products, whereas others have to be taken to a repair shop. Some products unfortunately are beyond repair or would cost too much to fix, and these are best either scrapped or broken down with parts to be reused. Fixing some products may be dangerous as they may contain electrical charge – in capacitors, for example.

Unwanted electronic and electrical equipment is the fastest-growing waste area. What happens to old games consoles, computers, CRT computer monitor screens, your old mobile phone? With the advanced development of technology, some electrical items quickly become outdated and consumers desire the latest technology. Are 3D flatscreen TVs set to replace 'normal' flatscreen

TVs? If so, what will happen to all of the older TVs? The need to change attitudes in how we repair or reuse products is enormous. How could this be achieved?

Rethink

Consider your lifestyle and that of others close to you, and think about how you buy products and the energy required to use them. Society is constantly evolving and changing, and you can evaluate how you could make a difference. Do you really have to have the latest mobile phone if your current one still works well and does everything you actually need? Can you buy products that are entirely made in this country so as to reduce the number of transportation miles? Can you design a product that uses a waste product or part to create a new product?

It might be useful to visit the websites listed in the Resources section below for further ideas on how designers are rethinking the designing of products.

3.2 Eco-design

This involves the whole system of looking at an end product, from design to finished product, and its use of materials and energy.

Eco-design is the process of considering the environment from the start when designing a product, and trying to minimise the damage caused by the product's life cycle. A designer must think through the main stages if the product is to be successful and acceptable as eco-designed. These main stages are:

○ product planning
○ product development
○ design process
○ functionality
○ safety
○ ergonomics
○ technical issues and requirements
○ design aesthetics.

The EU Ecolabel is an official label awarded to a product, guaranteeing it has fulfilled specific criteria (see Figure 3.12). A product awarded the EU Ecolabel will have been found to have a smaller environmental impact than other similar products. The EU Ecolabel is the official sign of environmental quality. It is awarded by independent organisations and is valid throughout Europe. The label's aim is to limit the environmental impacts of a product over its entire life cycle by looking at issues such as energy and water consumption, waste production and use of renewable resources.

△ **Figure 3.12** The EU Ecolabel

Knowledge link
More information on the 6Rs and environmental and sustainability issues relating to designing and making products can be found in Chapter 8.

Other useful resources
www.uk.freecycle.org
www.redesigndesign.org
http://biginjap.blogspot.com/2009/10/tetra-pak-lamp.html

Learning objectives

By the end of this chapter you should have developed a knowledge and understanding of:

- how to generate a wide variety of ideas, taking into consideration different possibilities of materials and processes
- how to approach being creative, innovative and adventurous in your ideas
- how to use a range of 2D and 3D techniques to communicate ideas
- how to check design proposals against a design specification
- how to produce formal/CAD drawings
- how to select and specify appropriate materials, quantities, sizes, tolerances
- identifying critical points for quality control and time scales in the manufacturing process.

Introduction

Finding initial design ideas can sometimes be a daunting task. One way in which designers approach this starting point is to search for design ideas/inspiration boards. What things do you like? What shapes, forms, colours, etc. do you like? Look at nature. Look at mathematical patterns. Look at existing products and conceptual products that you like. Look at what your user group likes.

Create inspiration boards around these themes to inspire you when you design; lay them out in front of you. Pick out some of the shapes, forms, colours, patterns, details to help you come up with initial sketches. Remember, after generating an initial sketch you have the opportunity to develop it thoroughly, so don't think that every sketch has to be perfect or a completely developed solution.

You will be expected to generate a range of feasible design ideas, based upon the criteria in a design specification. All sorts of sources can be used for inspiration – your design specification and research, of course, but you may also decide to base some aspects of your ideas on a theme, such as:

- natural forms – look around you at nature, animals, trees and plants, clouds, etc.
- the work of other designers or a design movement, e.g. Starck, Bauhaus, Newsom, Rams, Ive
- influences from music, films, media or current trends
- new technological developments, e.g. using new materials or processes, new smaller circuit boards, electronic developments.

You should come up with a range of feasible design ideas on a sheet. Your ideas *must* relate to your specification, so ensure the design specification is to hand so that you can see what it states. You should try to produce quickly sketched ideas, preferably in a mix of 2D and 3D. You should be considering colour, shape, form, texture, finish and materials in your sketches. This can be done through the addition of thorough annotation of all of your sketches with reference to the materials, finish, texture, etc., and use of a high level of design and technology-specific language – correct terminology.

You should generate your sketched ideas using appropriate media, and should try to demonstrate skills and techniques using that media, i.e. 2D sketching, 3D sketching, blue pencil sketching, fine line pen, coloured pencil, markers, Adobe Photoshop/Illustrator, etc. Your ideas should be produced quickly and they should communicate clearly, through sketching and annotation, what it is you are designing, i.e. make it recognisable.

You should also show evidence of the influence of research on your design ideas, which should not be a problem, as this should come naturally from the design specification, which is based upon research and analysis. As you experiment with first ideas and gradually refine your thinking, you should start to think about the possible materials or processes you could use, to work out whether your ideas are feasible. You may also start to play around with combinations of ideas or work on the fine detail of some of your ideas. The information you acquired during your research phase should enable you to develop and refine alternative ideas to the stage where you can select one or two that are the most promising to be developed.

4.1 Sketching techniques

A good 2D sketch is better than a poor 3D sketch! A 3D sketch is more difficult to produce; however, it will give more information on how the product will look. You will need to select the most appropriate sketching strategy/technique when generating design ideas. Whatever works best for you!

2D sketching

A 2D sketch is a good method of quickly generating a design idea as it will show what the product will look like from a single view (usually the front view). There are many ways to produce quick 2D sketches. The two main ones are to use a lightly sketched 2D crated rectangle as a starting point or to use a centreline if you are more confident. There are many other methods, such as 'in the mind's eye', but the two suggested here work very well and are used by professional designers.

A 2D crated rectangle is a great way to start. Begin by lightly sketching out a vertical line (this will become your centreline) and then sketch a rectangle around this centreline. This box is now your 2D crate with which you can sketch a design (see Figure 4.1).

3D sketching

As noted above, a good 3D sketch is difficult to produce. However, if you can create one, you can illustrate far more detail than in a 2D sketch as it will show three 'sides' of the product (usually the front, a side and the top view). There are techniques and strategies that you can use to help you sketch in 3D. The best of these is 3D crating. This is sketching out a cube that you can break down and use as a guide to sketch your design to realise it in 3D.

To sketch out a 3D crating box you should always attempt it in either isometric or two-point perspective as these will give the most real-looking sketches and result in a better communication method. Both methods start by lightly sketching a centre vertical line that becomes the closest corner of the box to the viewer (Figure 4.2). You then lightly add diagonal lines away from this centre line near the bottom and the top of the line.

If you sketch parallel diagonal lines, this will become an isometric box. If your diagonal lines are sketched so that they will eventually meet (at a vanishing point), this will become a two-point perspective box. You should then lightly sketch the vertical lines to create two sides of the box. Finally, where these vertical lines cross the top diagonal lines, you should lightly sketch diagonal lines which are either parallel or converge to the vanishing points to complete the 3D crating box. Figure 4.3 gives step-by-step diagrams.

Once you have a 3D crating box you can break it down to sketch various shapes and forms within the box guidelines to help ensure that your sketch is in 3D. Figure 4.3 shows examples of 3D sketches using a 3D two-point perspective crating box.

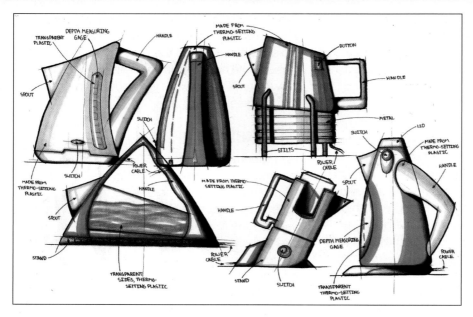

△ **Figure 4.1** Examples of 2D crating and sketching

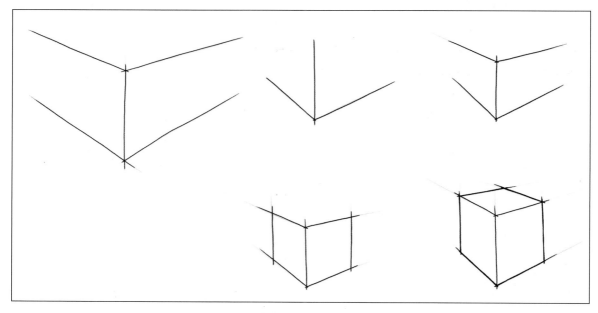

△ **Figure 4.2** Start by sketching a centre vertical line

Blue pencil sketching

Many designers use blue pencil sketching as a starting point on a design sheet as it can break up the 'daunting white space' that a design sheet can sometimes be. Initial quick ideas and thumbnail sketches can be added as a layer that will then be sketched over (but not traced!). This adds another dimension to sketched ideas as it gives the sheet different layers and details that the eye notices when focusing in on aspects.

A blue-coloured pencil will work but it is better to sketch with a 0.7 mm or 0.9 mm retractable pencil with blue leads as it is important that it always remains sharp to allow for differences in the weight of the blue line, i.e. emphasis can be placed in different areas (see Figure 4.4).

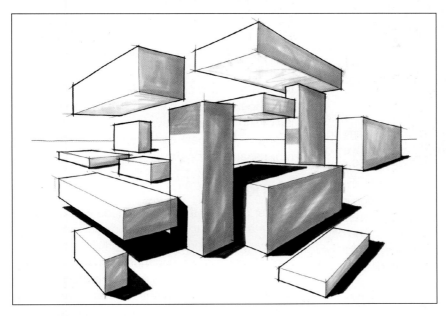

△ **Figure 4.3** How to sketch out a 3D crating box

△ **Figure 4.4** Blue pencil sketching

Fine line pen

The use of a black fine line pen cannot be underestimated in the communication of a design idea. A fine black pen can be used for many techniques, such as cross-hatching, thick and thin outlines, and sketching. Annotation can be completed using a fine black pen. A fine line pen is used by professional designers to communicate annotation and it is a common convention to use black.

Techniques such as thick and thin lines are often used to make an idea stand out more clearly on a page. It is a technique that is best employed on a 3D sketch, although it can also work effectively on a 2D sketch. The trick with thick and thin lines is to ensure that the outer edge of a design idea is a thicker black line and the inner lines are thin. This enhances the sketch and 'lifts' it off the page and draws the eye to the idea. It works well if the design idea is just a line sketch or rendered.

Coloured pencil and shading

When you add colour or shading to a sketch it is important that you try to use a technique other than flat colour. Pencil crayons allow you to add more or less tone to a sketch through the amount of pressure you place through the pencil onto the paper. The more pressure you add, the darker the tone. Techniques such as applying more pressure around the outside edge of a sketch and then easing the pressure off away from the edge add a very effective technique to a sketch (see Figure 4.5).

If you are adding coloured pencil to a 3D sketch, you should decide on which direction the light is coming from so that you can work out which surfaces will appear darker as they will be in more shadow (see Figure 4.6).

Markers

Marker pens are a more advanced way of adding colour and tone to a 2D or 3D sketch and can achieve professional results. Marker pens take a lot of practice and you must use the correct equipment if you want to achieve professional results. Correct equipment such as marker pens with a chisel tip, marker paper (normal paper absorbs the marker pen and the techniques do not fully work), a black fine line pen, a chinagraph

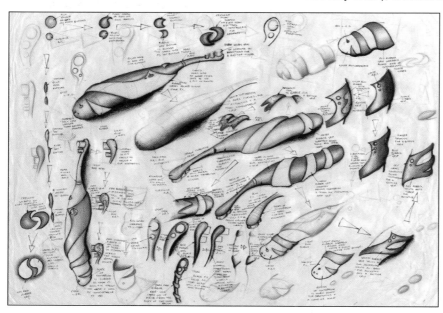

△ **Figure 4.5** Example of simple colour rendering technique

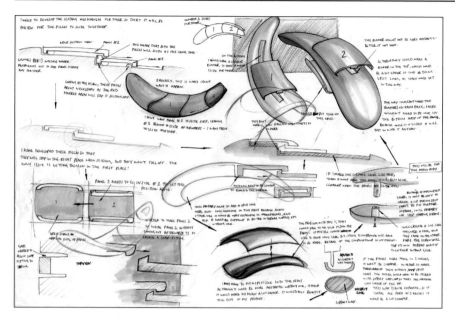

△ **Figure 4.6** Example of 3D colour rendering using pencils

pencil and a very soft black coloured pencil are all essential to achieve high quality.

You should follow similar rules to colour rendering when using marker pens. Markers allow you to go over them a number of times to add further depth to the work. Marker pens and all other equipment are available at many art stores.

Annotation

Annotation is used to describe, explain and discuss a design idea to improve your communication. It can express a lot of your design intent and is considered very important in the communication of an idea. Often a sketch does not show all of your design intent and this is where discussing your idea, on paper, can help your communication to the examiner.

You can draw particular attention to a part of a design idea. When describing your design idea, think about its shape and form. Does it resemble anything familiar, e.g. a known shape (an ellipse), another product, a famous building, something from nature? If you are explaining an idea you could mention what materials you are thinking it could be made from; what type or kind of finish it might have; how might the materials be joined together; why you have designed certain features such as rounded corners, holes or grooves. Imagine discussing your design idea with a friend, a family member, your teacher or your user group. What would you say? See Figure 4.7 for an example.

Putting it all together

When communicating and presenting design ideas, you should try to use a range of media, skills and techniques to help you, although you should choose the ones that you can use to best effect. Try not to perfectly 'lay out' your designs on a page. Sketch naturally and if an idea goes over the top of another idea, don't worry about it. Design ideas are supposed to be quick sketches, not perfect, precious final designs. The examples in Figure 4.9 show different pupils' approaches towards communicating design ideas for a range of products.

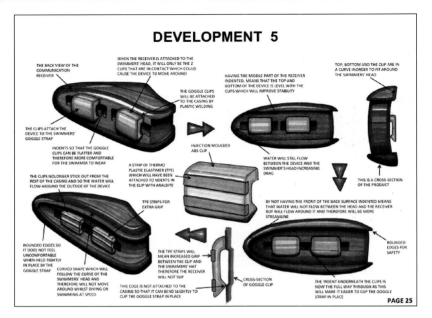

△ **Figure 4.7** Example annotation of a shape

Activity

Describe the example shape in Figure 4.8. Try to use D&T-specific terms in your notes.

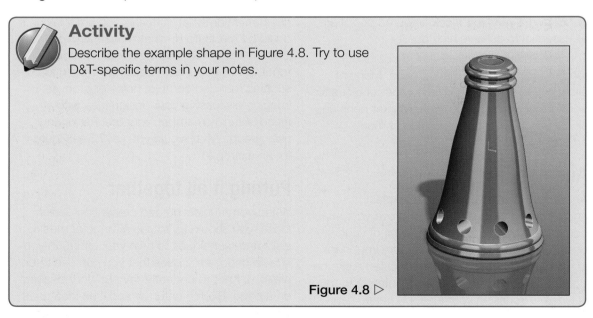

Figure 4.8 ▷

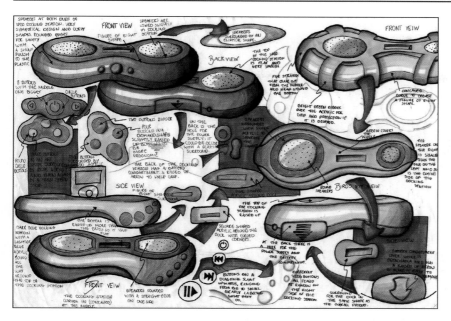

△ **Figure 4.9** Example design ideas sheet

4.2 **Evaluation of ideas**

Once you have produced a range of design ideas you should evaluate them against your design specification to see which ones are the strongest or best satisfy the criteria you set or have been set.

Your analysis of ideas against your design specification can be communicated in a variety of ways. You could use a video camera and lay out your design ideas, comparing them against the specification and commenting on how well each idea meets the criteria. Alternatively, you could use Post-it notes against each idea, evaluating the strengths and weaknesses of each idea against the criteria, of the design specification. If you have the facilities you could scan in all of your design ideas and then present them on a single sheet with an evaluative statement of which you feel meets the criteria most suitably.

You could also test your design ideas by asking your user group and/or others their opinions of your design ideas and how these meet the design specification criteria, before starting to develop an idea. You should be considering and commenting on constructional details, colour, shape, form, texture, finish, materials, etc. against the points listed in your design specification.

In the light of comments from your user group and others, you should reflect on how well your ideas have met the existing criteria. If the user group comment that they like the direction that one idea has taken, and it is different from the design specification, then you can consider modifying your design specification before commencing with development. Modify the criteria from the comments, evaluating why you are making the changes (this is really important and gains marks) and present an updated design specification identifying the changes.

Some design ideas can be complex and need to be reviewed in light of manufacturing constraints.

Controlled assessment link
Figure 5.20 on page 84 shows an example of a student's evaluation of design ideas.

You may have to reduce the number of parts to simplify the construction so it is possible for you to make the design with the facilities available.

Analysing a design for manufacture

At the point before selection of an idea for development you should consider a number of factors to check the feasibility of your design for manufacture. You should review your design ideas, considering how parts might join together. You may have sketched a complex design and you need to think through how it could be made of separate parts that join together. If your design has many separate parts you will need to think about methods of construction and how these individual parts can be 'fixed' together. What processes would you use? Do you know how to use any of these processes? Does your design use different materials? How can you join these different materials together? What manufacturing methods do you think you might use to make your design?

If you are unsure how you will make your design idea, perhaps you need to simplify the design to suit a method that you are already familiar with. Alternatively, you can research other methods of construction. Knowing a greater number of methods of manufacture allows you to be more creative with your design ideas. Understanding these methods enables you to think through where you might 'split' your design into separate components.

If your design has electronic parts inside, how will these components be held in place? Will this affect your design idea and how the parts might come apart to access the components?

Are you planning on manufacturing a number of your design ideas? Does your design allow for easy replication of parts? Will you have to design a jig or template to allow for lots of the same part to be accurately manufactured? Will you plan to use CAD CAM to manufacture your design and if so, what CAM method will be used? Does this CAM method allow for your design to be made?

Many CAM methods allow only for machining in a vertical direction and so undercuts or holes in sides of parts are sometimes difficult to manufacture using this method.

4.3 Development of ideas

Your aim should be to select and develop a chosen idea until you produce the best possible solution to the problem for your user group. In the first instance this will be done through 2D and 3D development sketches, looking at your initial ideas and analysis in greater detail and asking questions against the specification as you develop the design further. You should develop all areas of your selected design idea, investigating *all* of the finer details. To help you develop a design idea you should also use modelling to realise your design in 3D and make decisions as to the direction your development will take. As you develop models it is really useful to test your design with your user group to see how they respond to your idea.

At the start of your development you should select a design idea that you feel best solves the initial problem and will satisfy both the specification and your user group. There are a number of ways to start developing an idea – and there is no wrong way. Some designers like to start by sketching, in 2D and 3D, some possible developments of a chosen idea, focusing on the initial aesthetics and slight changes in form. Many designers then like to translate the idea into 3D so that they can start to realise the form and also test the idea. The advantage of modelling is that it produces a 3D model where all sides, the back and bottom have to be considered. A model can be held and tested for ergonomics by a user and then this information can be fed back into developing the design. Models can then be photographed and used to communicate more information as you can annotate the photos or even sketch over the top of them.

You should look to develop all aspects of a selected design. If, for example, you were designing a radio, you might consider some of the following: the battery compartment, knobs, dials, switches, speakers, speaker configuration, screen, layout of buttons, stand, positions, aerial, sizes, split lines, how parts fit/join together, lugs, snap fittings, how components are held in place, etc. At this point you could use some digital photos of details that you may have taken and include them on your development sheet as areas to be addressed, looking at the finer details and developing them for your design. This will allow for additional development research to be carried out, e.g. anthropometrics data (sizes) for dials/knobs/switches.

Your development should include the use of models (CAD, Styrofoam, MDF, card), which you can then photograph/print/cut out/use and develop further. For example, for a radio you could model the battery compartment/power source, at 2–3 times the scale, to show how that area is to be developed in your design/how a mechanism works (sliding, snap fit, rotating, etc.) and why it will be done in a certain way. You could also look at the type of texture/finish you wish to achieve. Your test development models should be finished to a good standard. You should use CAD to help you develop your design in 3D. You can create simple shapes/forms and then use these to draw/design over. CAD can also help you demonstrate how parts could fit together.

Your development should show a clear progression of your ideas at all times and you should annotate your designs honestly – you must discriminate/analyse/evaluate all areas of your design, stating what is good and bad, what works and what does not, and why.

In industry, modelling is a key process because it enables manufacturers to test and modify products and processes. Even though it may involve making a number of development models, in the long run it saves time and reduces manufacturing costs because products and processes are tried and tested before manufacture. This avoids costly mistakes such as the product not functioning properly or not meeting customer requirements. Sketched modelling techniques can include drawing exploded views, which can show details of how parts are to fit together.

As a product develops it becomes more accurate until it becomes a 'prototype product'. This is a detailed 3D model made from suitable materials to test the product before manufacture. Making a detailed 3D model it should help you plan:

o the most appropriate assembly processes – what order you are going to make things in and why

o how long different processes might take – get on with other jobs instead of waiting for a particular machine

o the materials, components, equipment and tools you need

o the order in which to assemble your product

o how easy the product will be to manufacture in the time available – do you need to simplify anything?

o where and how you will check the quality of your product – quality assurance/quality control checks against your working drawings/production plan/design specification.

Modelling

A 3D model is excellent for working out ergonomics, form and practical details, such as how different parts of the product will be joined together. Modelling materials should be used rather than a resistant material as these should be easier and quicker to cut, shape, form and join. Popular materials for modelling are corrugated card and blue Styrofoam. Both are readily available and relatively cheap. Both can be quickly formed and shaped to realise a design in 3D. A model can be made to scale (either bigger or smaller: twice size, half size, etc.) or made approximately to the same size as the final model.

Virtual

Digital media and new technologies have developed enormously over the past few years and designers at all levels have been quick to use these methods for both designing and making. There are a number of 3D modelling software choices for designers, such as Pro/ENGINEER (now known as Creo Elements/Pro and replacing Pro/Desktop in schools), Solidworks, Inventor, Solidedge, SpaceClaim, GoogleSketchUp, Catia and many more.

These software systems allow photorealistic 3D models to be produced and rendered (see Figure 4.10). The software can be used to develop design ideas and can be invaluable in visualising what a product will look like when it is made. It is excellent for checking the proportions of a product, trying out different colours and materials, placing the visualisation into a scene, and being able to quickly modify the design to re-render.

△ **Figure 4.10** Example virtual renderings and product development (Pro/ENGINEER 5.0)

Card

Corrugated card is a commonly used modelling material because it is widely available in a range of thicknesses and easy to obtain. Most designers will use recycled boxes, which makes the material even cheaper to use. It can be cut using scissors, a scroll saw or a craft knife. It can be joined easily using PVA glue, masking tape, Sellotape or double-sided tape.

△ **Figure 4.11** Corrugated card model

Styrofoam/foam modelling

Cutting and shaping high-density polystyrene foam, or Styrofoam as it is more commonly known, is a fast way of creating solid models to make sure that you get the size and shape of your final product right. Styrofoam is available in a limited range of colours and the most common is blue. It is supplied in large, flat sheets of different thicknesses, ranging from 15 mm through to 100 mm. It can be cut easily using a range of hand tools such as a coping saw, finishing materials such as abrasive paper, and some power tools such as a scroll saw. Final shaping and finishing can be achieved using files and abrasive paper such as 'Wet and Dry' paper.

◁ **Figure 4.12**
Examples of Styrofoam models

Constructional kits

You could use a technical construction kit such as Meccano or Lego Technic to simply work out some 'block' forms. Many of these kits have things such as gears that can be used to test and develop mechanisms before implementing them into a design. It might give you an idea of sizes of gear trains, for example.

△ **Figure 4.14** The ZCorp 310

△ **Figure 4.13** Example Lego mechanisms

Rapid prototyping

Several systems are now available that enable components to be made directly from designs drawn on a computer. These machines do not cut out the component from a solid block of material, but build up the shape by adding material. These machines are additive rather than subtractive (such as a 3D CAM router).

There are many different materials available at a range of prices, depending on what functional requirement is needed from the model. Rapid prototyping is an expensive technology and some models can cost many thousands of pounds. Some machines, such as the ZCorp 310 (Figure 4.14), use a binder to solidify layers of powder together to form the model. Other machines use ABS plastic, cured acrylic, rubber, vinyl or layers of resin (Figure 4.15).

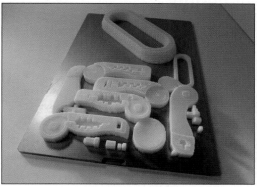

△ **Figure 4.15** ABS, acrylic and STL

Computer software processes a CAD model into very thin layers (0.07–0.2 mm) that a rapid prototype machine can build. The most accurate and precise models are built from a greater number of layers that are extremely thin (0.01 mm) and so provide a higher degree of precision. These machines, and subsequent models, are far more expensive and tend to be used only by industry. Some machines can cost close to £500,000. Many people think rapid prototyping is used only for final models, but it can be used to develop models before final production.

△ **Figure 4.16** Dyson model and student test models

Laser cutters

Laser cutters are an excellent way of cutting sheet, card and manufactured boards. They work by vaporising the material along a very narrow line (around 0.15 mm). These machines are very good for making professional models quickly. Design can be drawn in CAD (2D or 3D) and then linked to a laser to output layers of material that can be built up to form a model. The examples in Figure 4.17 show some MDF test mechanism models that have then been finished using hand tools and power tools.

◁ **Figure 4.17** Example models

Client testing

One stage of the development process is to test how well the product idea does the job it was designed to do. You need to make an assessment of how well the proposed developed idea performs against each point on the design specification and what the user group thinks about the design. Some points will be easier to test than others and this is where you will benefit from a range of models. Some points of the design specification will be harder to evaluate at this time and you will only be able to record user group opinion. You can gather opinions either through interviews or a questionnaire.

Through this testing you should be able to determine what you need to do to finalise a solution that satisfies your design specification and matches your user group criteria.

Selection of materials

Selecting the right material for your product can be difficult and is often one of the most crucial decisions in determining the success or failure of any design. The final decision is often a case of selecting a material with properties that are the best compromise of a number of conflicting requirements and best suit the intended function.

Many products are made up of a number of components or parts. The material for each part should be considered separately, as one material may be ideal for one part but unsuitable for another. Often a combination of materials and the different aesthetics and properties of each adds appeal and value to the product. You must consider that some materials are easier to join together than others. A material's aesthetics will have a major effect on the final appearance of the product. You could, for example, use the aesthetic qualities of the beautiful grain of a piece of solid timber combined with a perfectly brushed surface of a piece of aluminium sheet. The combination of these two materials may give a very modern appeal.

One of the first considerations is the environment in which the product is to be used. Many materials deteriorate quickly when used outside and this could affect your product if you are specifically designing for the outdoors. You also need to consider whether a material will fit in with the environment it is designed for. Will it look right?

You will need to consider the demands placed upon the material in terms of its physical properties, such as material strength, hardness and durability. What about the cost? Are you planning to use an expensive material? Materials are usually available in standard stock form and could be expensive if you are using only part of the material.

Activity

Identify the material properties that might be important for each of the following applications. For each application, put the properties in order of priority, from the most important to the least important:

(a) the frame for an off-road mountain bike

(b) a tyre for a racing bike

(c) the body of an electric kettle

(d) a chair for use in a classroom

(e) a table for use in a school canteen

(f) a helmet for a cyclist

(g) a car bumper

(h) a satellite dish

(i) the body panels on the space shuttle.

Exam tips

You should use the names of properties when you are explaining why you have decided to choose a certain material for a particular purpose.

Constructional details

You will need to show all the relevant information to enable your product to be made. It is not important how this information is recorded and communicated, but it will require a combination of drawings and notes. You will need to show details of the following.

Formal drawings

You should clearly illustrate your final design proposal to show what your product will look like, how it will work and how it will be made. You should use an appropriate graphic style. You must annotate your design proposal, using appropriate technical language identifying the materials, finish, components, systems and construction processes required to manufacture your product, in relation to your chosen scale of production. This may require you to produce exploded views to explain any design detail. Your annotation should demonstrate an understanding of the working characteristics of your chosen materials, finish, components, systems, equipment, processes and technology.

You could present your final design proposal as follows:

o A presentation drawing, to the user group, showing 3D views of your final design idea, including relevant annotation.

o A sheet presented in orthographic standard showing all faces of your final design idea, i.e. front, side, top, back, end views (elevations) (see Figure 4.19).

You should relate your annotation back to your specification, perhaps with sub-headings. You should show an awareness of industrial processes, for example how you would make a certain part in industry, such as knobs/dials – mass produced, injection moulded, etc.

CAD drawings and renderings

If you have access to CAD software you could 'render' your final design to help communicate further your design intent. All CAD software programs have a rendering option allowing materials to be assigned to parts. The design can then be lit and placed into environments to be rendered. There is also a variety of third-party rendering software programs and CAD files can be transferred into one of these to render your product. One advantage is that materials can quickly be changed and you can experiment with combinations of materials until you settle on an appropriate choice (see Figure 4.19).

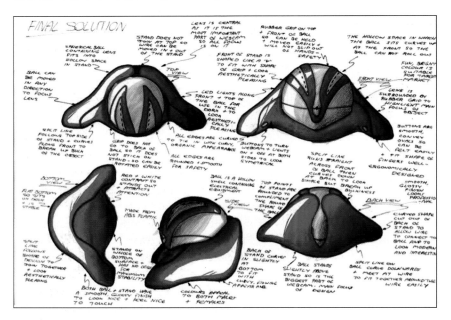

△ **Figure 4.18** Example of a final design proposal

△ **Figure 4.19** Examples of CAD renderings from pupils

4.4 Planning for manufacture

Planning for manufacture is a critical part of design development and is something you should be thinking about during the latter stages of development. You need to think through how to manufacture your final design solution, selecting the most appropriate materials, sizes and quantities of materials. You should consider whether you would need to make use of any control devices or create your own (jigs, templates) to aid the repetition of making some parts.

Thinking ahead and recording all the stages of production and the order in which they are to be carried out is called production planning. In larger-scale industry a project manager would be employed to fulfil this role. Many use sophisticated and complex software, such as Arena, to aid planning on this scale. You can also use simple ICT software as most programs have pre-drawn planning symbols built in.

Writing a production plan

A good production plan will include a list of the stages of making the product, in order, the materials, tools, machines and manufacturing processes to be used. It should also highlight any safety issues at each stage and give an estimate of how long each stage will take. It is important to record when quality control and assurance checks (QC/QA) are needed.

A production plan or plan of manufacture means choosing the best, safest and most cost-effective method of production, the best layout for equipment and people (if you were making multiple parts on a production line or working in industry), the best materials for your product and the best way to control product quality at each stage. A production plan is a key part of your (a company's) quality system because it documents each stage of manufacture. This enables checks to be made for quality, so each component of the product, or multiple parts, is made to the same standard. A production plan

also enables faults to be identified and provides feedback so that changes can be made to the production plan, if necessary.

Thinking through the stages where you will need to add feedback opportunities is key to an excellent production plan.

Preparing a production plan – tables

A good way to start a production plan is to make a list of all the stages you think are needed to make each part of the product and then put them into a table (see Figure 4.20). Your table could have headings such as: Stage no. (list in the order you think you will have to manufacture), Part (what part of the product you are making), Material (what material you are planning to use), Size (how much material is needed), Stock size of the material and supplier (does the material come in flat sheets and what size? Will you need more than one?), Description (what will be involved), Tools/equipment/machines.

Knowledge link
To help you decide on specifying appropriate materials, go to selection of materials in Chapter 1.

When specifying the appropriate material you should reference suppliers' catalogues (available from your teacher) or websites to find out standard sizes of materials and the cost. You should then work out whether this affects your product and whether you have to modify your plan.

If you are struggling to work out how much material you will need then it is a good idea at this stage to practise manufacturing your product by making a full-size Styrofoam model. You should gain an understanding of your ability to manufacture your final design in relation to your expectations for your product. If your ability falls below your requirement, you have two options: either improve your skills or adapt the

Production Plan – Mood Lamp

Stage	Part	Material choices	Size	Stock size / Supplier	Qty.	Description	Tools / Machines
Materials needed / order materials	Main Body – front & back Lamp head Lamp inserts	Mahogany, Zebrano, Iroko, Sapele? Ash, Beech, Olive wood Aluminium sheet, acrylic, Laminate	150x350 x40 90x75xx 75 170x240 x3	Garstang Timber, Lancaster Saw Mills, K&M, Timber suppliers Hindleys, K&M, Technology supplies, Techsoft	2 1 2	Need to machine front and back on the 3D Router to get shape and hollow out inside. Lamp head to turn on wood lathe Lamp inserts on Laser cutter	3D Router Wood lathe Laser cutter
Mark out / prepare materials	Cut timber to size for Router bed & Lathe Cut 3mm sheet for laser cutter	Sapele Olive wood blank 3mm silver acrylic sheet	150x350 x40 90x75xx 75 170x240 x3	Same as above	2 1 2	Cut and square off timber for 3D router. Run program simulation Find centre's of Olive wood Remove protective plastic film from acrylic	3D Router Wood lathe Laser cutter
Machine materials	Front & Back machined on Boxford A3HSRi Turn Lamp head on Wood lathe Set up paths for Laser and cut acrylic sheet	Same as above	Same as above	Same as above	2 1 2	Put work onto machine bed. Check settings & depth. Machine parts Fix Olive wood between centres' and turn to shape Set toolpaths and colour depths on Laser.	Same as above
Detail materials	Clean up tool paths. Drill holes for speakers Clean up edges. Remove frame marks. Round edges of Lamp head. Drill holes for GU10 pins.	Same as above. Need 3mm, 6mm & 10mm drill bits. Need 25mm Forstner bit	Same as above	School drill bits.	N/A	Cut off frame to hold work on Boxford. Files off edges. Clean up tool path marks. Drill holes for speakers using 25mm Forstner bit. Part off Lamp head from Wood Lathe. Drill holes for GU10 pins and wires to connect.	Same as above
Finish materials and assemble parts	Sand front and back using rough / medium / smooth (240) Glasspaper's. Finish with wax. Glasspaper Lamp head and finish with varnish.	Glasspaper grades 1, 1.5, 240 Wax	As above	Hindleys, K&M, Technology Supplies	N/A	Glasspaper front and back parts using rough / medium / smooth glasspaper. Finish with wax. Glasspaper Lamp head and finish with varnish.	Vertical linisher Cork block

△ **Figure 4.20** Example of a planning table

process. Adapting the process should result in an easier or simplified model. You can then measure all parts of your planning model and use these to specify your material choice.

Preparing a production plan – flow charts

Once you have completed a table of planning, the stages of making your product can be put into a flow chart (see Figure 4.21), and quality control and quality assurance checks can be added where you think they will be needed. You need to produce a clear flow chart that explains how to manufacture your product, within realistic deadlines. Realistic deadlines are those that are achievable. You should match the making of the product to the time available.

The work that you have already done on developing, modelling, prototyping and testing should help you to plan your product manufacture using a flow chart. You should have a clear idea of an assembly order of the different component parts since completing your table. You should produce a work order/work schedule as a flow diagram (see Figure 4.21). In your flow chart you should identify:

- o the order of assembly of the various components
- o tools, machines and equipment to be used
- o assembly processes
- o the estimated time each stage of manufacture will take
- o key stages of the manufacture where quality is checked and feedback opportunities are given
- o safety requirements.

If your product is to be manufactured using CAD CAM you may have a number of smaller parts that will need to be made through other processes. Remember in your planning that you can often get on with making these components while you are waiting for the 'body' of your work to be machined. Examples of quality assurance and quality control could be:

- o checking to see whether a piece of material has been cut to the correct length
- o checking to see whether parts join together correctly (tolerance)
- o checking whether a part has been finished to the necessary standard.

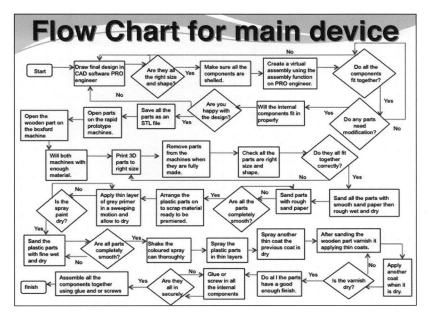

△ **Figure 4.21** Example of a flow chart for production planning (utilising CAD CAM)

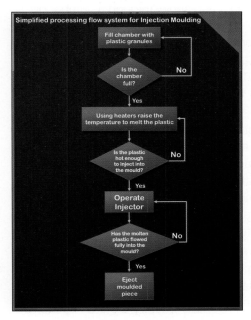

△ **Figure 4.22** An example of a simplified material processing system for injection moulding

Flow charts use standard symbols that describe the nature of the activity. These symbols are commonly available to use in all Office software. The symbols shown in Figure 4.23 are the main ones that you will need to use.

Beginning or end

Process

Decision

△ **Figure 4.23** Flow chart symbols

Quality control and quality assurance

Quality assurance is the checks carried out before a product is made and the systems used during its manufacture to make sure the product is produced to the required standard. Quality control is the checks carried out after the product has been made to ensure that it is of the required standard.

Methods to aid accuracy and repetition in manufacture

Control devices are made to enable one product to be made to a very high standard or to enable multiple copies of a product to be made quickly, easily and the same. Examples of control devices are:

○ a pattern to be used in a vacuum-forming machine
○ a pattern from which a sand casting could be made
○ a stencil
○ a template
○ a jig (for drilling, bending, assembling components, joining materials, etc.).

If a control device is needed to enable your product to be made, you will need to plan its manufacture. More information about control devices is covered in Chapter 13.

△ **Figure 4.24** A drilling jig for multiple cams for an automata

Working drawing

A working drawing or 'engineering' drawing gives enough information to allow a third party or machine to manufacture your product. It should contain all of the relevant dimensions of your product and show, through a number of 2D views from above, front and side, all of the necessary information about your product. You can add more views than the three mentioned as, the more information that is available, the easier it will be for a third-party manufacturer to understand your design.

In industry it is becoming common practice to include a 3D working drawing alongside the 2D orthographic drawing as new developments in CAD software allow for mark-ups to be placed in 3D and saved as PDF files that can easily be shared. Measurements should always be in millimetres.

You will need to produce a working/engineering drawing, either accurately hand drawn or through the use of CAD software (most have a wizard) such as Pro/ENGINEER (Creo Elements Pro), Solidworks, Inventor, Pro/Desktop, etc. You should monitor the accuracy of your manufacture as it progresses, checking against the dimensions and tolerances you detailed in your working drawing(s). If you have modelled parts of your product using CAD, it makes sense to produce your working drawing using the software. You may wish to print two copies of your working drawing, or photocopy it so that you can place parts against the drawing to check accuracy of size while keeping one copy 'clean' for your folder.

The materials used for even the most common objects that we use every day are chosen because of their properties. For example, the material used for a toilet has to have good compressive strength so that people can sit on it without it breaking. It also needs to have good corrosion resistance and a smooth surface so that it is easy to clean.

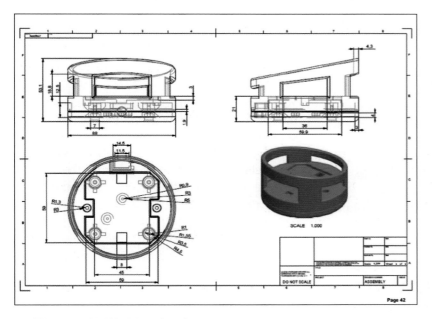

△ **Figure 4.25** Working drawing

Learning objectives

By the end of this chapter you should have developed a knowledge and understanding of:

- the appropriate techniques and processes to make your own products
- the evaluation process and how to take into account the views of others
- how to test against a specification and ensure your product is suitable for the intended user.

Introduction

When designing your product it is important to consider the manufacturing techniques available to you. All processes allow you both opportunities and limitations. If you understand these you can use this information to guide you through the development process and produce a high-quality product.

5.1 Aesthetics

The various processes that you will have access to will have an effect on the aesthetic qualities of your design. Some of the techniques will give an accurate and high-quality finish, others will leave a more natural and rugged appearance.

The complexity of your product will also guide you in your choice of manufacturing technique. Vacuum forming will allow you to form plastic into a variety of shapes, but if your mould involves 'undercuts' or fine detail these may stop it from being released from the formed plastic sheet after the process is complete. If you need to produce a cylindrical wooden object, the obvious choice would be a lathe as the spinning motion of this piece of machinery is designed to allow the user to produce cylindrical and conical shapes easily.

Cost

Your choice of manufacturing technique can have a dramatic influence over the cost. An example of this is rapid prototyping. This process can give an exceptionably accurate product, but the costs involved can be 5–10 times the cost of more traditional materials processed in more traditional ways (see Figure 5.1).

Customer/client

When working through a design project you will normally start with a brief. Within this there may be clues to a particular manufacturing technique that your client or customer would prefer. If you are looking for a more traditional product then using natural timbers and wood joints would be suitable; a more contemporary product may call for a type of plastic manufactured using a vacuum former or laser cutter.

Environment

Environmental concerns can be divided into two camps – the environment the product will 'live' in and how the product will affect the natural environment (the 6 Rs). We will deal with these separately.

Where a product will spend its life has a big impact on your choice of process. For example, if a product is to be used in a kitchen or bathroom it may need to have a waterproof finish and waterproof joins.

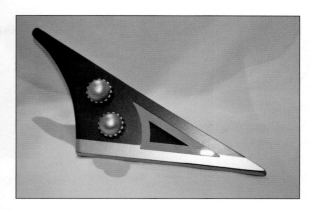

△ **Figure 5.1** Products are manufactured in different ways depending on the environment in which they are to be used.

△ **Figure 5.2** Living in a bathroom

As a planet we are now paying more attention than ever to our 'environment'. Consumers will choose products based on how environmentally friendly they are. You should consider using recycled or reclaimed materials in your designs or even choosing manufacturing processes that create very little waste.

Size

The size of your product can potentially limit your choice of manufacturing technique. Some pieces of equipment, such as vacuum formers (see Figure 5.3) and CAM routers (see Figure 5.4), have a maximum size that they can cut. You will

need to check this before you decide to use any of these machines.

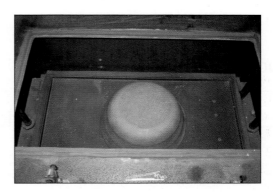

△ **Figure 5.3** A vacuum former and mould

△ **Figure 5.4** A 3D router with material

Safety

Health and safety should be taken into consideration throughout the design process. You should only ever use a piece of equipment or attempt a technique when you have been fully trained in how to use it safely.

Function

What does your product need to do? You should repeatedly ask yourself this question. The manufacturing technique you choose can allow the product to work effectively or severely limit its functions.

If you require a strong, tough, durable and water-resistant product, choosing a powder-based 3D printer to manufacture the main casing would be a big mistake – this process will result in an accurate and detailed product but it will be very fragile.

△ **Figure 5.5** Broken RP models

Materials

One of the biggest factors when choosing your manufacturing technique is the material that you are working with. Having an understanding of the properties of materials will allow you to pick a suitable process. For example, certain plastics, such as PVC, cannot be laser cut due to the toxic fumes released, which are harmful to humans and will also corrode the machinery.

Student Exemplar

Specification

Client

•The product I am going to produce will cost between £18-£22.

•This money will be spent on the materials I will be using such as plastics. Also I will have to buy the LED bulbs for my lamp.

•The product will take approximately 40 hours to make.

•Most of the time is used to design the product and then to manufacturer it to a high standard.

•The lamp will be designed to the highest standard and then filed and sanded down to create a clean, sleek finish with no marks.

User

•My chosen user group is teenagers, aged 13-19.

•I have chosen this group because I can relate to this group the most and I understand what they look for in a product.

• I have to ensure that my designs are modern and in-fashion in order to appeal to this audience.

• I will also try to incorporate some designs and colours that are popular in teenager culture now, such as blackberry designs and pink/blue colour schemes.

• The lamp will have only one button but that will be designed to fit the users finger to ensure comfort and good ergonomics.

•The lamp will be unisex, so the colours will be neutral to ensure this.

Manufacturer

•The body of my lamp will be made from moulded plastic. The shaped plastic will be formed by the 3d miller which will shaped the plastic in 2 halves and then I will glue and smooth down the join.

•The plastic will be smooth and rounded, in a curved shape.

•The lamp will have LED bulbs inside to create a mood light.

• Also there will be no toxic finishes or paints used in these design.

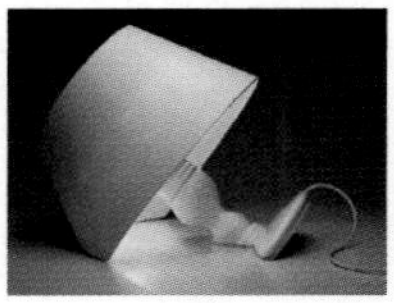

Designer

• My lamp will be based on the theme of post modernism.

•The Post modernism era contains very simple plain designs so I will incorporate the smooth, curved edges into my design to make it look more free-flowing and sleek.

•The lamp will have LED bulbs inside which will change colour. Therefore this lamp is solely for the purpose of providing a subtle mood light in a bedroom or living room environment.

•It will have a single switch and the lights will change colour to create a mood light.

•This product has been designed to be placed on a table or bedside table. Therefore the product has to be quite small and not bulky in order to fit on the table.

• I will keep the colours neutral because most of the post modernism designs use colours such as creams, whites and light grey's.

△ **Figure 5.6** Specification page

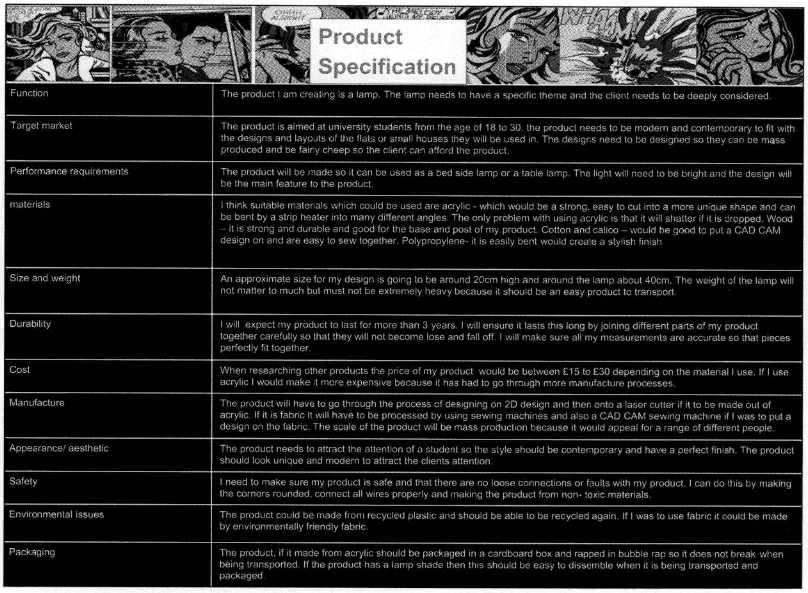

Product Specification

Function	The product I am creating is a lamp. The lamp needs to have a specific theme and the client needs to be deeply considered.
Target market	The product is aimed at university students from the age of 18 to 30. the product needs to be modern and contemporary to fit with the designs and layouts of the flats or small houses they will be used in. The designs need to be designed so they can be mass produced and be fairly cheep so the client can afford the product.
Performance requirements	The product will be made so it can be used as a bed side lamp or a table lamp. The light will need to be bright and the design will be the main feature to the product.
materials	I think suitable materials which could be used are acrylic - which would be a strong, easy to cut into a more unique shape and can be bent by a strip heater into many different angles. The only problem with using acrylic is that it will shatter if it is dropped. Wood – it is strong and durable and good for the base and post of my product. Cotton and calico – would be good to put a CAD CAM design on and are easy to sew together. Polypropylene- it is easily bent would create a stylish finish
Size and weight	An approximate size for my design is going to be around 20cm high and around the lamp about 40cm. The weight of the lamp will not matter to much but must not be extremely heavy because it should be an easy product to transport.
Durability	I will expect my product to last for more than 3 years. I will ensure it lasts this long by joining different parts of my product together carefully so that they will not become lose and fall off. I will make sure all my measurements are accurate so that pieces perfectly fit together.
Cost	When researching other products the price of my product would be between £15 to £30 depending on the material I use. If I use acrylic I would make it more expensive because it has had to go through more manufacture processes.
Manufacture	The product will have to go through the process of designing on 2D design and then onto a laser cutter if it to be made out of acrylic. If it is fabric it will have to be processed by using sewing machines and also a CAD CAM sewing machine if I was to put a design on the fabric. The scale of the product will be mass production because it would appeal for a range of different people.
Appearance/ aesthetic	The product needs to attract the attention of a student so the style should be contemporary and have a perfect finish. The product should look unique and modern to attract the clients attention.
Safety	I need to make sure my product is safe and that there are no loose connections or faults with my product. I can do this by making the corners rounded, connect all wires properly and making the product from non- toxic materials.
Environmental issues	The product could be made from recycled plastic and should be able to be recycled again. If I was to use fabric it could be made by environmentally friendly fabric.
Packaging	The product, if it made from acrylic should be packaged in a cardboard box and rapped in bubble rap so it does not break when being transported. If the product has a lamp shade then this should be easy to dissemble when it is being transported and packaged.

△ **Figure 5.7** Specification page

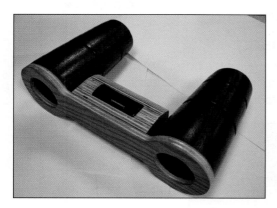

△ **Figure 5.8** Development of a design proposal with consideration of manufacturing technique

△ **Figure 5.9** Development of a design proposal with consideration of manufacturing technique

△ **Figure 5.10** Development of a design proposal with consideration of manufacturing technique

Evaluation of your own ideas for development

When examining your own work for possible developments it is vital that you take into consideration four groups of people:

○ the client
○ the designer
○ the manufacturer
○ the user.

Activity

For each of the following manufacturing techniques list two advantages and two disadvantages that could influence your choice of process during the practical phase of your coursework:

(a) 3D printing

(b) vacuum forming

(c) milling

(d) hand-cut wood joints

(e) laser cutting

(f) lathe turning

(g) casting.

Each of these people or groups of people has particular needs or wants from the product (see Figure 5.11).

Client

The client is the boss! This is the person who instructs or employs a designer to come up with a product that will fulfil a particular role. When

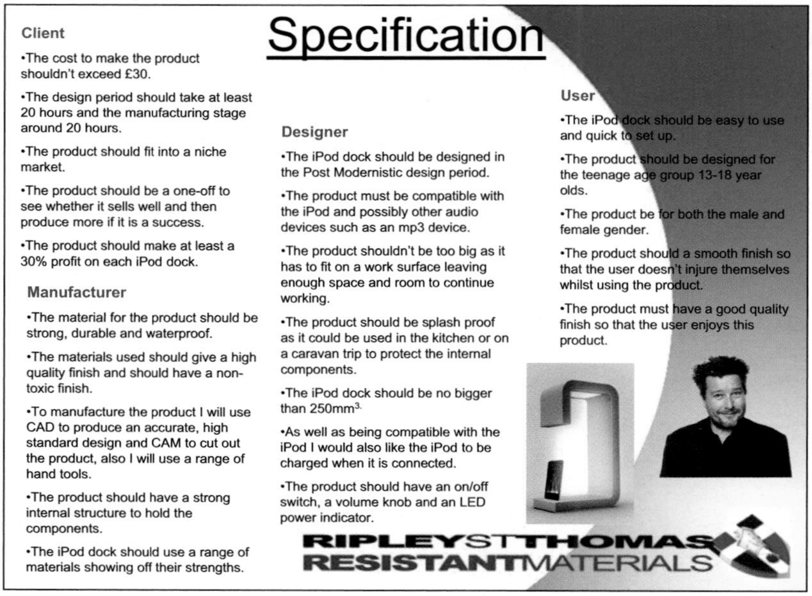

Specification

Client

•The cost to make the product shouldn't exceed £30.

•The design period should take at least 20 hours and the manufacturing stage around 20 hours.

•The product should fit into a niche market.

•The product should be a one-off to see whether it sells well and then produce more if it is a success.

•The product should make at least a 30% profit on each iPod dock.

Manufacturer

•The material for the product should be strong, durable and waterproof.

•The materials used should give a high quality finish and should have a non-toxic finish.

•To manufacture the product I will use CAD to produce an accurate, high standard design and CAM to cut out the product, also I will use a range of hand tools.

•The product should have a strong internal structure to hold the components.

•The iPod dock should use a range of materials showing off their strengths.

Designer

•The iPod dock should be designed in the Post Modernistic design period.

•The product must be compatible with the iPod and possibly other audio devices such as an mp3 device.

•The product shouldn't be too big as it has to fit on a work surface leaving enough space and room to continue working.

•The product should be splash proof as it could be used in the kitchen or on a caravan trip to protect the internal components.

•The iPod dock should be no bigger than 250mm³.

•As well as being compatible with the iPod I would also like the iPod to be charged when it is connected.

•The product should have an on/off switch, a volume knob and an LED power indicator.

User

•The iPod dock should be easy to use and quick to set up.

•The product should be designed for the teenage age group 13-18 year olds.

•The product be for both the male and female gender.

•The product should a smooth finish so that the user doesn't injure themselves whilst using the product.

•The product must have a good quality finish so that the user enjoys this product.

RIPLEYSTTHOMAS RESISTANTMATERIALS

△ **Figure 5.11** Design sheet with specification broken down into the four design groups

considering how their opinion will affect the way in which your design develops you should keep in mind their prime concerns:

○ cost of manufacture
○ time scales for design and manufacture
○ does the product have to fit with a particular style?
○ does it appeal to the identified consumer group?

An interview early in the project will give you an insight into your client's thoughts. It is also worth revisiting your client at various points to get feedback on idea sketches or prototypes that you have built. These can be recorded on your design work in the form of client comments (see Figure 5.12).

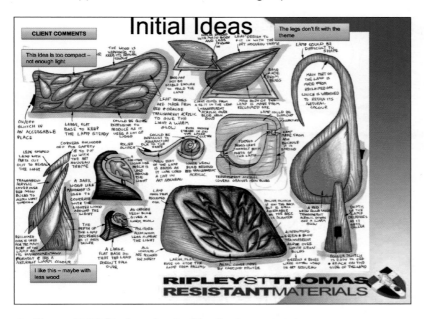

△ **Figure 5.12** Design sheet with client comments

Designer

The designer obviously designs the product (see Figure 5.13). They are responsible for ensuring that the product meets the needs of the other groups so will consider:

○ aesthetics
○ ergonomics
○ materials
○ functions
○ safety features
○ environment/green issues.

Manufacturer

The manufacturer is responsible for the way in which the product will be made. It is important that consideration is given to the manufacturer; if the product is designed to be over-complex or with features that cannot be produced with the equipment available, it becomes useless and the project will hit a dead end. When producing your designs, consider:

○ what equipment is available
○ is it appropriate with the chosen materials?
○ is it viable in the allotted time?
○ is the quality of the product at an acceptable level?

Figure 5.14 shows the design for a manufacture portfolio sheet.

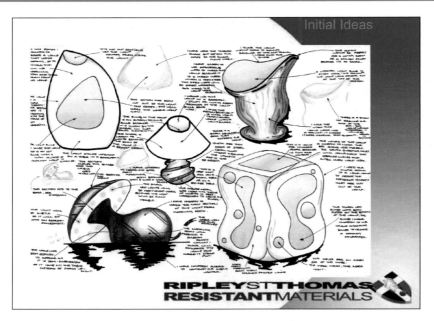

△ **Figure 5.13** Initial idea sheets

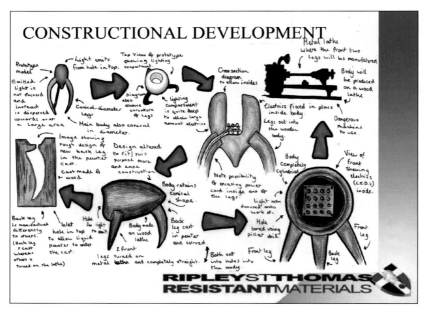

△ **Figure 5.14** Design for a manufacture portfolio sheet

User/consumer

This is the person who will ultimately be buying or using the product. It is massively important that you design and produce a product that they want to have. The success or failure of any product lies with the consumer. The client and designer will have identified who the user is. They must then compile information on:

- habits
- interests
- hobbies
- typical income
- products they buy.

Throughout the design phase of your coursework always keep in mind the four groups of people listed on page 78. It's very easy to fall into the trap of designing for yourself, but ultimately the most successful designs are those that take into account the client, designer, manufacturer and user.

Analysing and evaluating your product

Testing and evaluating your designs can be done throughout the project. It is important to ensure your work is suitable for your intended user, meets your specification and is also of a high enough standard to compete against commercially available products.

There are a number of ways to test various parts of your designs. The following are some of the most suitable.

Physical modelling and prototyping

This is one of the best ways of developing your work. Once you have come up with some initial ideas, make a model of one or some of them. You can use any material you wish for this (Styrofoam and card tend to work well). When you have finished a model it will help you visualise your designs three dimensionally and you can also use it to test whether components will fit.

△ **Figure 5.15** Consumer/user boards

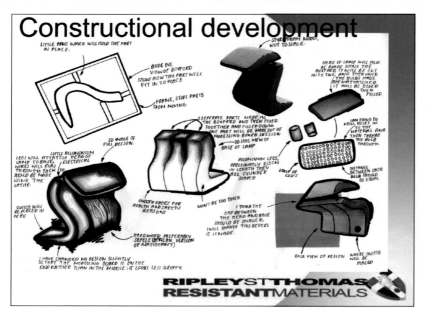

△ **Figure 5.16** Prototype development sheets with mixed media work

A good tip is to use a digital camera to photograph your model. This image can then be printed and used in your development sheets as a starting point for your modifications. The image can be sketched over with pencil or fine line pen to show the changes you want to make.

CAD modelling

CAD can be used in development in much the same way as a card or foam model. It can allow you to visualise a design in 3D and also test the size for components, etc. Some of the more advanced CAD packages will also allow you to 'render' your model with any material. You can then test which one would look best, and on the very advanced software even test which material will be strongest or which shape most aerodynamic.

Physical bench testing

If you are unsure of anything, test it! For example, if you need to select an appropriate finish for some timber, try out a few different types on some scrap wood. Always photograph any

◁ **Figure 5.17**
CAD modelling

testing that you do – these pictures serve as great evidence in your portfolio (see Figure 5.18).

When you have completed your project you should always test your product in a range of ways, trying to emulate its working life. Whatever you designed it to do, test that it actually does it. Remember to photograph this as well or even video it if you are producing an e-portfolio.

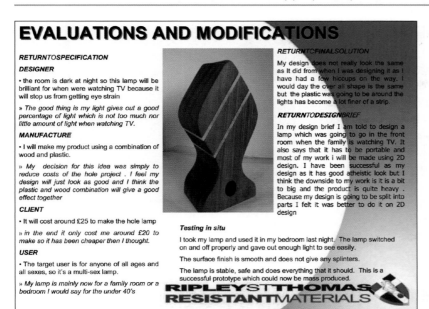

△ **Figure 5.18** Test your product and keep the evidence

Interviews and questionnaires

These can be carried out before and after the project. They are a great way of getting feedback from clients and consumers, but they are only as useful as the questions you ask. Always plan what information you need to get and then write your questions to search for this information (see Figure 5.19).

△ **Figure 5.19** It's all in the question

Testing against a specification

On completion of your project it is important to check your final product against your specification. A good way of doing this is to use each point of your specification as a heading and then write whether or not you have succeeded in achieving this statement (see Figure 5.20). It is not always necessary to have a final product that achieves every point of the specification, so long as you can justify why the product has deviated from this. Often you will discover during manufacture that you need to make modifications for a range of reasons – you will not be penalised for this.

Activity

For each of these products write up what you think the user would want from the product:

(a) desk lamp

(b) bedside radio

(c) mood light

(d) iPod dock

(e) coffee table

(f) media storage rack.

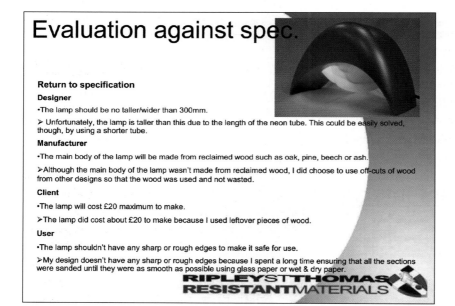

Evaluation against spec.

Return to specification

Designer

•The lamp should be no taller/wider than 300mm.

➤ Unfortunately, the lamp is taller than this due to the length of the neon tube. This could be easily solved, though, by using a shorter tube.

Manufacturer

•The main body of the lamp will be made from reclaimed wood such as oak, pine, beech or ash.

➤Although the main body of the lamp wasn't made from reclaimed wood, I did choose to use off-cuts of wood from other designs so that the wood was used and not wasted.

Client

•The lamp will cost £20 maximum to make.

➤The lamp did cost about £20 to make because I used leftover pieces of wood.

User

•The lamp shouldn't have any sharp or rough edges to make it safe for use.

➤My design doesn't have any sharp or rough edges because I spent a long time ensuring that all the sections were sanded until they were as smooth as possible using glass paper or wet & dry paper.

**RIPLEYSTTHOMAS
RESISTANTMATERIALS**

△ **Figure 5.20** Evaluating against the specification

chapter 6
Social and cultural influences

Learning objectives

By the end of this chapter you should have developed a knowledge and understanding of:

o the effect of society and culture on designing and making
o the impact of products on lifestyle.

Introduction

Designers don't just think about how well their products work and what they look like. They have to consider a much broader range of issues, such as how our values and culture will affect both the design and how it could be made. They also have to think about how the products will affect the way that we live.

This chapter outlines how the values of society and culture affect the choices made during the design and making of products. It also outlines how products can have an impact on our lifestyle.

6.1 Social influences on design

When designing a product, the designer's main aim is that it meets the needs of the user and the market. We often interpret this as how well the product does what it was designed to do and how it looks. However, the society that we live in has certain beliefs and expectations. Unless the design also takes these into consideration, the product may not be successful.

These social influences cover many parts of the designing and making process. They affect choices such as:

o who needs to use the product
o what it will be made from
o where it will be made
o who will make it.

These influences are not permanently fixed. They will change over time as the expectations in society change. Often the designer will have to consider more than one influence, with the choice being based on what society values as more important at that time.

Who needs to use the product?

The design brief should identify the target user of the product. If the designer creates a product that will meet the needs of the average user, this will probably mean that many people might not be able to use it.

This is because the average user with an average-sized body and average capabilities does not represent the full range of users. There will be users who are smaller than average, who are bigger than average, or who have limited physical capabilities.

Society has an expectation that products should be designed so that they can be used by those who have physical disabilities. These include the visually impaired and blind, wheelchair users and the elderly, who may not have the strength and dexterity of the young. This is known as inclusive design. Here are some examples.

o Light switches, door handles and lift buttons should be positioned at a height where they can easily be used by people in wheelchairs.
o The stop and start buttons on machines should not just be green and red. This would make it difficult for people who are colour-blind or visually impaired to use them. They should include lettering or symbols to show their purpose.

o Traditional 'turn handle' taps can be difficult to use for people who do not have a strong grip. This often includes many of the elderly. An inclusive design alternative would be wrist action taps operated by a lever (see Figure 6.1).

△ **Figure 6.1** Wrist action tap, operated by a lever

> Key term
>
> **Inclusive design** – designing a product so that it can be used by all members of society.

What will the product be made from?

In recent years, people have become increasingly aware that our environment is affected by how we use materials. This ranges from pollution caused by obtaining materials to how we dispose of the materials when we no longer use a product.

Case study

Disposable plastic bags were introduced at supermarkets in 1977. Before that, customers used paper bags and cardboard boxes. At that time, our society welcomed the use of plastic bags as they were cheaper, stronger and more resistant to damage from water.

Currently, across the world, each year about 4,000,000,000,000 plastic bags are used.

The plastic used to make the bags is made from oil. Obtaining oil can involve drilling underground or under the sea, transporting the oil many miles and chemical processing, known as refining. There is a risk of pollution, such as oil spills, during each step of this activity. Further, oil is a non-renewable resource. This means that there is only a certain amount of oil that we can use, and we will eventually run out of it.

Once they are finished with, most bags are thrown away. This can cause pollution. Many are buried in waste dumps. Many are dumped

at sea – it is estimated that 100,000 marine animals are killed each year by plastic bags.

The values of society are changing because of concerns about how our use of materials is affecting the environment. To reduce the number of plastic bags required, bag designs have been changed so that they can be used more than once. People are also increasingly using reusable bags made from natural materials, such as linen, or even returning to use paper bags again (see Figure 6.2).

△ **Figure 6.2** Reusable eco-friendly carrier bag

Increasingly, society expects that products will not be wasteful in their use of materials. Also, products should use materials that cause as little damage as possible to the environment. This might mean using sustainable, natural materials or it might mean using materials that can be recycled at the end of their usable life.

Using alternative materials can mean that products need to be redesigned, as the materials have different properties. It can affect the cost of products, due to the cost of the material or the processes that must be used to form them into products.

Key term
Pollution – contamination of the environment.

Who will make the product?

As a society we all want low-cost, high-quality products. For products that are required in large numbers, one way of achieving this is to automate the manufacturing processes. This means using robots or machines, rather than people, to make the products (see Figure 6.3).

Using robots might mean that a product costs less to make and has consistent quality. However, it also means that there will be fewer jobs for people. If fewer people are working there might be fewer who are able to buy the product.

△ **Figure 6.3** Manufacturing using robots

Where will the product be made?

A large part of the cost of most products is the labour time needed to make them. Labour costs vary from country to country. For example, the average wage paid to workers in the UK is approximately 60 to 70 times that paid to workers in India.

Some companies have tried to achieve these savings by moving activities from the UK to countries with lower labour costs. This applies equally to making products or providing services, such as call centres. However, the working conditions and safety laws in some of these countries may be below those that are accepted in the UK. Some might even exploit child labour. In the case of products, they may also need to be transported back to the market where they are to be sold. This can have both financial and environmental costs.

The designer has to judge whether society values the lower cost of the products as more or less important than the approach chosen to make the product.

6.2 Design influences on lifestyle

As well as considering how the values of society influence design, the designer should also consider how the product they are designing may affect society and our lifestyle.

For example, 60 years ago most homes did not have a television. The first televisions showed only black and white pictures, on tiny screens. Less than 30 years ago, there were only three television channels available in the UK. Now we might have large-screen colour systems with hundreds of channels available.

This has had a huge effect on our lifestyles. People have access to entertainment in their own homes, so they may be less likely to go out. This has an affect on the number of people going to bars and cinemas. It also has an effect on traditional pastimes, such as needlework or learning to play music. Television also allows advertising into people's homes, which changes their wants and expectations.

As another example, MP3 players are often used on public transport (see Figure 6.4). They let people choose what they want to listen to. However, they can also have negative aspects.

○ People using them may not be able to hear announcements about safety or the destination reached.
○ Other passengers might find the background noise from these devices irritating.
○ There are possible health issues. The hearing of people using MP3 players could be damaged if the volume is too loud.
○ Some people also argue that they reduce the amount of communication between people.

The designer has to think about these negative effects and may change his design to reduce them.

△ **Figure 6.4** Using an MP3 player

6.3 **Cultural influences**

Culture is the way that history, beliefs and tradition have influenced a group of people. Normally the group shares a common interest and has similar values. This might range from all living in the same country to religious beliefs or the type of music they all like.

Culture has a big influence on the products that the people in that group use. This might range from the type of building they live in to the type of clothes they wear and the things that they value

in a product. This can affect both the need that a product is designed to meet and the appearance of the product. Here are some examples.

○ In the UK, it is traditional to eat dinner sitting at a table. In Japan, the tradition is to eat dinner while sitting on the floor (see Figure 6.5). As a result, Japanese dining tables have very short legs!
○ In South Africa red is the colour of mourning. However, in China it symbolises good fortune. The response of these two societies to the same red product may be very different.
○ In the Middle East and Africa, products might be valued as more attractive if they have traditional patterns or designs on them. In Europe and the USA, the influence of industrial design can mean that greater value may be awarded to a simple design without a pattern.
○ Animals can be seen in different ways by different cultures. In Europe, piggy banks are often given to children to encourage them to save money. However, in some Middle Eastern countries pigs are regarded as unclean, and presenting an image of a pig to a person could be an insult.

Designers have to consider the cultures of all the potential users and markets for a product, not just their own. Each market may have different cultural values that will influence the design of a product.

△ **Figure 6.5** Japanese dining table

Key term

Culture – the history, beliefs and traditions of a group of people.

Activities

1. A company is designing a mobile phone for use by the elderly. They have asked you to tell them what social influences they should consider when designing and making the phone. Write them a letter, explaining each of your suggestions.

2. Different countries are often associated with different types of vehicle. For example, pick-up trucks in the USA, sports cars in Italy, tuk-tuks in Thailand, rickshaws in China, and gondolas in Venice.

   Using the internet, find pictures of the typical vehicles used in a range of countries. For each one, explain how it meets the needs of that society and how it has been influenced by their culture.

Controlled assessment link

The ideas discussed in this chapter will be relevant to your Controlled Assessment work. The design brief in Figure 2.11 clearly considers the target user of the product (social influences on design) and states that the design should have a South African or Aboriginal theme (cultural influences on design).

chapter 7
Consumer choice

> ### Learning objectives
> By the end of this chapter you should have developed a knowledge and understanding of:
> o how to identify the factors involved in consumer choice
> o how to carry out market research to establish consumer preferences of target market(s)
> o how to use market research information to influence the design.

Introduction

Different target markets have different needs. To gain an understanding of their needs market research is carried out. There are many different ways in which to carry out market research.

This chapter outlines a range of market research strategies and how they can be used to influence the design of a product.

7.1 Why have market research?

Everybody is different, with different needs and tastes. An example of this can be seen when you think about your family: do your grandparents or even parents spend all of their time on the same hobbies and pastimes as you? The answer is probably not. This is because they are a different age and generation, and have different tastes and levels of fitness to you. To a designer they are a different target market to you.

△ **Figure 7.1** Identifying the target market

>
> ### Key term
> **Target market** – a clearly defined group who will be the users of a product.

> ### Exam tip
> When you have identified your target market in your Controlled Assessment make sure you gather your market research from a target market suited to the genre.

It is important to consider the needs of the target market when designing a new product. To gather information about the needs of the target market, market research is carried out. Through market research potential customers may be introduced to the idea of a new product and their opinions recorded.

Market research is important to a designer for the following reasons.

o It enables the designer to discover whether the target market will be willing to purchase the product.
o It allows the designer to determine how much the customer is willing to pay for the product if it were produced.
o It helps the designer estimate how many units/products will sell.

○ It aids the quality and suitability of the product as the target market can suggest improvements and/or modifications.

Key term

Market research – potential customers may be introduced to the idea of a new product and their opinions recorded.

7.2 Types of market research

Sometimes designers need to access large quantities of data to discover the target market's needs; on other occasions they may need more in-depth responses from a small sample of people from the target group. Depending upon designers' needs, market research can be carried out in a variety of ways.

Telephone

Sometimes companies 'cold call' potential customers. 'Cold calling' is when a company phones members of the public randomly to ask questions. Customers are asked several questions about the product. 'Cold calling' is often frowned upon as it can irritate potential customers if they are phoned at an inconvenient time.

△ **Figure 7.2** Telephone market research

Postal questionnaire

Postal questionnaires are not as common as they were in the past. This is due to the ease and speed of online questionnaires. Postal questionnaires are useful to collate information about generic questions, for example whether people would buy the item. The information from postal questionnaires is collated and used to create a general average response. The disadvantage of postal questionnaires is that they can be costly and can take a long time to collate. The key findings from a postal questionnaire are often followed up in an interview or focus group.

△ **Figure 7.3** Postal questionnaire market research

Online questionnaire

Online questionnaires are cheap and easy to set up. Customers can easily be targeted across a wide geographic area. They are asked general questions about the product, for example what price they are willing to pay for it. The results are collated in a similar way to postal responses. An advantage of online questionnaires is that they are fast and customers have the option of whether or not to opt in. Customers are often enticed into responding by being entered into a prize draw. A disadvantage of online questionnaires is that responses are often only in a tick box format without room for personal opinions. The key findings from an online questionnaire are often followed up in an interview or focus group.

△ **Figure 7.4** Online questionnaire market research

A focus group

A focus group of prospective customers will get together to discuss the pros and cons of the design idea. An advantage of focus groups is that the designer can ask in-depth questions, for example what suggestions do they have for improvement. A disadvantage of focus groups is that only a small proportion of the potential target market can be included.

△ **Figure 7.5** Focus group market research

Interviewing potential customers

A potential customer may volunteer to be interviewed about the design concept. This may happen when they are approached at a conference or a show and asked their opinions, or perhaps approached in the street and shown a simulation or photo of the product. An advantage of interviews is that the designer can ask in-depth questions and show the potential client prototypes or simulations to obtain an in-depth response. A disadvantage of interviews is that only a small proportion of the potential target market can be included.

△ **Figure 7.6** Interviewing potential customers

7.3 How can market research be used to influence design?

Market research is an essential part of the design process. Throughout the design and prototyping stage a design concept is being refined, modified and improved. Market research helps the design evolve quickly while keeping the needs of the target market in mind.

For example, if a young designer were asked to create a product to help an elderly person open tin cans in the kitchen, they may not be aware of the difficulties associated with the task without discussing it with a suitable potential client. Through market research the designer will be able to identify the problems the potential customer has and develop a product that is suitable for them. They will gain an insight on cost, size, weight, grip, etc. through their market research.

△ **Figure 7.7** Identifying the target group's needs and difficulties

Activity

Identify a target market and what market research you would carry out for the following products:

(a) a necklace inspired by nature

(b) a children's push-along toy

(c) a skateboard

(d) a traditional bird table

(e) a range of kitchen utensils.

Controlled assessment link

You will need to consider the target market and needs of the user as part of your Controlled Assessment work. Figure 2.15 on page 40 shows a student's questionnaire, which has been used to gather market research from the target market.

chapter 8
Consumer rights legislation, product maintenance and codes of practice

Learning objectives

By the end of this chapter you should have developed a knowledge and understanding of:

- the legal requirements regarding consumer rights and codes of practice relating to the safety of the products you design
- the sustainability and environmental issues connected with the design and manufacture of products
- the 6Rs – repair, reduce, recycle, reuse, rethink and refuse
- the economic and human costs concerned with the design and manufacture of products.

Introduction

When designing and making a product there are many things we need to consider. These range from environmental issues to consumer rights, and from ethical issues to product maintenance.

This chapter outlines the basics in consumer rights legislation and codes of practice. It also aims to summarise environmental, sustainability, moral, economic and ethical issues that a designer needs to consider when planning a new product.

8.1 Consumer rights and legislation

When you go shopping or hire a service (such as a plumber) there are laws in place to protect the customer from purchasing an unsafe product or service. These are known as consumer rights and legislation. There are many different types of consumer law and protection, each with a different focus but a common aim – to protect the customer.

The most common aspects of consumer rights legislation are described below.

The Sale of Goods Act

Whenever you buy anything, the product is covered under the Sale of Goods Act. This means the product must be fit for purpose, as described and of reasonable quality.

'Fit for purpose' means the product must be able to do the job it is intended to do. An example of this is before you buy a mobile phone accessory you would ask the assistant whether it would work with your model of phone; the sales assistant must answer correctly, otherwise they would be breaking the law under the Sale of Goods Act.

'As described' means that the item must match the description that the seller has written. The description may have been read by the buyer in something like a catalogue.

'Reasonable quality' means that the product is free from defects or problems, safe to use, and that its appearance is good and finished to a satisfactory level.

The Trade Descriptions Act

The Trade Descriptions Act is similar to the Sale of Goods Act. It focuses on the idea that the product must match any descriptions available of the product written by the seller. It is against the law for the seller to make false claims about the product.

The Weights and Measures Act

The Weights and Measures Act means that it is against the law for sellers to sell their product short-measured or underweight. An example of this is if you purchase a 12 fl oz glass of lemonade in a restaurant as advertised in the menu, then the waiter must ensure that the glass is filled to at least the 12 fl oz mark otherwise they will be breaking the law under the Weights and Measures Act.

The Consumer Safety Act

The Consumer Safety Act enables the government to prohibit the sale of any products it deems to be dangerous.

The Consumer Protection Act

The Consumer Protection Act is aimed at preventing the sale of any unsafe or faulty products.

Fire safety regulations

There are many parts to fire safety regulations. The most recent addition is the rule that an employer is responsible for ensuring that a workplace is safe at all times and that they carry out assessments to prove this. In the context of resistant materials, fire safety regulations are in place to stop the sale of poor-quality furniture that may cause a fire risk.

Protection for the designer

Many people think it is only the customer who needs laws to protect them from malpractice. Designers and inventors also need legislation, to protect them from having their ideas copied by others and losing out on potential custom.

It may cost money and be very time-consuming for a designer to have their idea/design protected, but once it is registered with the Intellectual Property Office no one can duplicate the design without their consent.

There is a range of ways in which a design or invention can be protected. These include patents, trademarks and copyright.

Patent

A patent is used to protect new inventions. It may be used to protect the design, how it works or how it is manufactured. A patent lasts only five years from the filing date but can be renewed for up to 20 years. After 20 years the patent usually becomes public property. Like property, a patent can be sold, mortgaged, given away or even abandoned. A patent protects the designer/inventor from having to worry about people stealing their ideas.

Trademark

A trademark is a symbol that is used to protect a company name, image, slogan, logo or a combination of these. Once the trademark is registered no other company may use the name, image, slogan or logo on their products. A trademark is put in place to protect a company from having less reputable companies using their signs and giving them a bad reputation.

Trademark: **TM**

Registered trademark: Ⓡ ◁ **Figure 8.1** Trademark symbols

Copyright

A copyright is an automatic protection for any original design, writing or artwork. It is free in the UK and in many other countries. Copyright infringement is when someone breaks the terms of how they may use the protected materials.

 ◁ **Figure 8.2** Copyright symbol

Activity

Read each of the situations. Which consumer legislation could the buyer use to complain about their faulty product?

1. Jennifer recently bought a digital camera. The camera specification states that it can be used with any computer made after 2005. Jennifer's computer was manufactured in 2010 but when she plugs her new digital camera into the computer the computer displays 'unknown device'.

2. Asma bought her little sister a soft toy. When she returned home she noticed the seam was loose and the soft toy had a hole in it.

3. Daniel bought a 500g box of chocolates, and when he got home he decided to weigh it. The box of chocolates weighed 485g.

8.2 **Codes of practice**

To ensure products on the market are safe, many are checked and tested. Although each company may have good intentions, the tests they conduct could vary from company to company, making the whole process pointless. To ensure the tests they carry out are of equal standard, manufacturers conform to a series of checks and tests devised by either the British Standards Institution, Conformité Européenne or the International Standards Organisation.

British Standards Institution (BSI)

If a company follows and passes the agreed tests and specification for a product or service, the product may be awarded the Kitemark symbol. The Kitemark scheme is a self-regulating and constant process that shows that the product meets the relevant standards. The Kitemark is a British symbol that shows the product has been tested to nationally acknowledged standards.

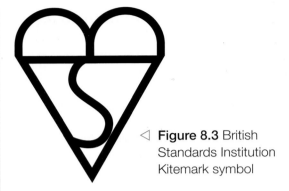

◁ **Figure 8.3** British Standards Institution Kitemark symbol

Conformité Européenne (CE)

The Conformité Européenne (CE) institution is very similar to the British Standards Institution. It is an institution that produces guidelines for the testing of products. The difference between the BSI and the CE is that the CE tells the buyer that the product meets the minimum requirements for the European Union, not just the UK. Products that have met the standards of the Conformité Européenne may hold the CE logo.

◁ **Figure 8.4** Conformité Européenne symbol (CE)

International Standards Organisation (ISO)

The International Standards Organisation is very similar to both the British Standards Institution and the Conformité Européenne. It again is an institution that produces guidelines for the testing of products. The key feature is that it shows whether products have met international standards. An example of a product conforming to such standards is a piece of A4 paper. Have you ever wondered who decided that each piece must be 210mm × 297mm? The answer is the International Standards Organisation.

Activity

Identify whether the following products are renewable or non-renewable:

(a) Pine

(b) Cotton

(c) Acrylic

(d) Pewter

(e) Mahogany.

8.3 Sustainability and the environment

When designing and making a product it is important to consider the effect it will have on the environment. Sustainability is about meeting the needs of the world without causing a detrimental effect on the environment.

All raw materials are taken from the world in some manner. These can be categorised into two groups. These are renewable resources and non-renewable resources.

Renewable resources are materials that can be replenished by the environment. For example, if we use timber we can plant more seeds to grow more trees, and if we use wool from a lamb the wool will grow again.

Non-renewable resources are materials that cannot be replenished, and once we have used them all then there will be no more. These are generally materials that come from the ground such as oil, iron and other metals.

A way of maintaining a constant supply of trees is a method called sustainable forestry. A lumberjack cuts down a tree but as he does so he plants at least one new seed to replace it. This will mean there is a constant supply of trees and therefore timber.

Key terms

Renewable – a raw material that can be reproduced through a natural process.

Non-renewable – a raw material that, once used, cannot be replaced.

8.4 The 6Rs

When designing a product or even contemplating whether a product is at the end of its life cycle, we need to consider the 6Rs. The 6Rs stand for repair, reduce, recycle, reuse, rethink and refuse.

Repair   *Technician*

The idea of 'repair' is asking the question when a product breaks down or no longer works properly – can you have it mended or do you need to buy a new one? Why not try to have it repaired?

Reduce

Can you use fewer raw materials and less energy? The term 'reduce' is to make you think about what resources you are using and try to cut down on them.

Recycle

Many materials can be used over and over again; however, too often they end up in landfill sites. Recycling is a great way to reprocess a material or item to do the same or a different job. If you see one of the two symbols in Figures 8.5 and 8.6 on an item it means that it can be recycled.

◁ **Figure 8.5** Recycling symbol

◁ **Figure 8.6** Green Dot recycling symbol

Some items have symbols on them that tell the user exactly what material they have been manufactured from. This helps the user to recycle the product at a recycling plant in the correct container.

Reuse

Can you use all or some of the parts of the product again? If you can, you will help reduce the amount of materials having to be produced.

Rethink

Do you waste a lot of products? Rethinking the number of products we need and the number of products manufactured could save the environment.

Refuse

'Refuse' is when an individual refuses to buy products or materials from companies that they think may be harming the environment. A person may, for example, refuse a product due to excessive material use or packaging.

Knowledge link
More information on the 6Rs and how they relate to sustainable design can be found in Chapter 3.

Student Exemplar

In this example you will see the pupil has considered how each part of their final prototype will be manufactured. Within this they have considered the materials used and the processes used in manufacture, and how these may impact on the environment. The pupil has also used this page to highlight any health and safety issues associated with the manufacturing process.

Glass

Please put this in a bottle bank

Aluminium

Recyclable aluminium

Steel

Recyclable steel

Mobius Loop

This is capable of being recycled

Plastics

PETE
Polyethylene terepthalate

HDPE
High-density polyethylene

V
PVC

LDPE
Low-density polyethylene

PP
Polyethylene

PS
Polystyrene

OTHER
All other resins and multi-materials

△ **Figure 8.7** Recycling symbols used in resistant materials

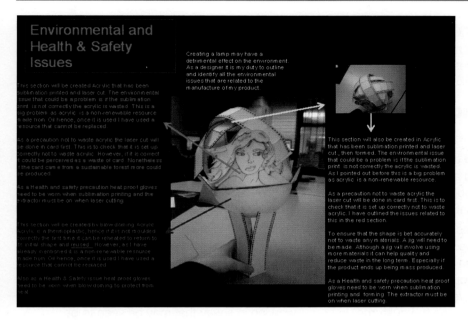

△ **Figure 8.8** Exemplar environmental considerations

8.5 **Planned obsolescence and the product life cycle**

Planned obsolescence is essential in keeping companies in business. If a company creates a product that becomes unwanted or is broken after a few years then customers will go out and buy a new product from it. This keeps the company in business. However, this can also have detrimental effects on the environment as many products will be sent to landfill sites as the manufacturer updates products to sell. If the manufacturer built products that lasted much longer this would be better for the environment; however, ultimately the manufacturer would have less business.

Product life cycle is when a product is introduced to the market and, as time goes on and it becomes less successful, the manufacturer decides to remove it from the market. Some manufacturers choose to redevelop the product and relaunch it, giving it a second life cycle. This process may be repeated; however, at some point new technology might make the product obsolete.

Key terms

Product life cycle – the stages a product goes through from outset to removal from the market and decomposition.

Planned obsolescence – the term used to describe products that are designed to have a limited lifespan to make customers buy a new version.

8.6 **Alternate energy**

The modern world depends on energy to power our businesses, homes and industries. Often such energy is created by burning fossil fuels (gas, coal and oil). However, we are slowly running out of these natural resources, and efforts are now being made to use alternative energy sources.

Knowledge link

For more information on alternative energy sources, look at Chapter 3.

8.7 **Moral, economic and ethical issues**

The modern world is a global society. Many products are designed and manufactured in different countries throughout the world and then sold on multiple international markets.

Sadly some companies exploit less economically developed countries by moving manufacturing tasks to them, which are then carried out in poor conditions and environments and for very little money. Some of these companies charge the customer in the UK a lot of money for the product when it costs them only a fraction of the price to manufacture as the workers receive low wages to make it. These are sometimes referred to as 'sweatshops'.

Ethical companies are those that care about the conditions of their employees and ensure their conditions are satisfactory in all aspects from production to distribution. Ethical companies ensure employees are working in a safe environment, have basic labour rights (for example, regular breaks) and are paid fairly.

Fairtrade

The FAIRTRADE Mark (see Figure 8.9) on products shows that workers have benefited from internationally agreed standards.

®

◁ **Figure 8.9**
FAIRTRADE Mark

The Fairtrade Foundation is the independent non-profit organisation that licenses the use of the FAIRTRADE Mark on products in the UK in accordance with internationally agreed Fairtrade standards.

It is not only employees and the environment we need to consider when designing new products. We also need to consider the moral issues concerning the product. An example of this is production-line automation. Is it morally right to have machines making products for a company, meaning many workers are redundant?

There are many moral, ethical and environmental issues concerned with the design and manufacture of products. Pressure groups are organisations that set out to change public opinion, and the practices of companies working in a way that may be seen to be morally controversial. Pressure groups try to influence people's perceptions through protests, advertising, petitions and reports. Pressure groups include organisations such as Greenpeace.

Activity

Visit the local supermarket. How many different products can you find bearing the FAIRTRADE Mark? What types of products are these? Where do you think they originated?

8.8 **Product maintenance**

Product maintenance is a necessity for many products to ensure they work efficiently. If a product is not maintained regularly then it may break. This could mean that, rather than paying for regular maintenance checks, the consumer must pay much more to replace the product. Product maintenance checks depend on the type of product, the environment in which it is used and the needs of the user.

There are many different maintenance checks that could be done; each will depend on the product.

However, there are some common product maintenance checks. These are as follows.

Changeable parts

Many products have changeable parts to stop the user having to buy a whole new product each time a small part breaks or wears out. A common example of this would be batteries in a games console. Usually the user would expect these parts to break or cease functioning first and would probably have spares available.

Occasionally some parts need replacing when they are wearing out but before they break, for example car tyres. When tyres start to become worn they need to be replaced to ensure there is good grip between the vehicle and the road.

Some products need to be changed annually even if they are not broken, to help the product run smoothly. An example of this would be an oil change in a car.

Lubrication

To reduce the wear caused by two surfaces rubbing against each other, lubrication is used. Lubrication is often a liquid or gel that aids the surfaces as they glide over each other. Lubrication is used in many items and a common example is oil. Oil is often used to stop metal parts from rubbing against each other. It is also used to protect the exterior of metals against rust.

Activity

List all the parts you would need to check when undertaking annual maintenance for the following products:

(a) a smoke alarm

(b) a push bicycle

(c) a car

(d) assembled flat-pack furniture

(e) a squeaky garden gate.

Learning objectives

By the end of this chapter you should have developed a knowledge and understanding of:

o   how the safety of the individual is essential
o   how to take responsibility to ensure that hazards are minimised and the working environment is safe to use
o   which health and safety regulations are required when working with tools, equipment, components and materials, including the use of personal protective equipment (PPE).

Introduction

When a new product is designed it is essential that it is manufactured safely. This chapter will focus on the health and safety implications during manufacture. It looks at the different risks in resistant materials and how they can be minimised.

9.1 **Personal responsibility for safety**

In the workshop there is one person who is responsible for your safety. That person is YOU. Workshops are very dangerous places but if you take your health and safety seriously then they are exciting places to be in.

Before undertaking any activity in the workshop you need to consider the following.

o   Is the environment safe to work in? The working environment should be well organised so that there is plenty of space to undertake tasks safely. The workshop should be well lit and a comfortable temperature. Emergency stop buttons and machine signs should be clearly displayed.

o   Do I have the appropriate attitude to work? Calm, sensible and focused is the only way to work. If you are distracted while using tools or machinery you may end up being seriously hurt.

o   Am I using the correct equipment for the task? Many accidents occur in the workshop as people try to use the wrong equipment to undertake a job. Each tool has a specific use and must only be used to do that task.

o   Do I need any personal protective equipment (PPE)? Many tasks require you to wear PPE, such as safety goggles.

 Key term

PPE – personal protective equipment is specialist equipment used to help protect a person undertaking a particular task.

9.2 **Machine safety checks**

When machinery is required in the workshop it is important that it is safe to use. To ensure the machine is safe the following points are essential.

o   Regular safety checks are made. This job is probably done by your teacher or technician on a daily basis. They check that everything is in the correct place and the machine is working correctly.

o   Visual inspection. Before you use a machine you should visually inspect it yourself. Are there loose wires? Is the tension right on a fretsaw? Is the drill piece in straight on the pillar drill? Is the machine guard covering the tool? If you are in any doubt you should not use the machine, and inform your teacher or technician.

o Instructions about how to use the machine should be clearly visible. Nonetheless, before you use any machinery you should have received training on how to use it safely.

o Emergency stop buttons should be visible and unobstructed.

o When faulty machinery is evident it must not be used and must be clearly labelled as such. If possible it should be removed from the workshop.

o Warning signs are provided. These usually specify what PPE is required to use the machine, i.e. safety goggles.

As well as regular checks it is important that some machines have their own in-built health and safety precautions. These include dust and fume extraction and machine guards.

Dust and fume extraction is essential to remove unnecessary fumes and dust from the user area. The dust or fumes created by the machine may harm the user through inhalation or by getting into their eyes. Extraction machines are used to prevent this by being attached to the main machine. Examples include laser cutters and disc sanders (see Figure 9.1).

A machine guard's primary purpose is to protect the user. If a machine guard is not fitted or used correctly there is a risk that the user may come into contact with the moving parts, for example if their tie got caught in a pillar drill. It also prevents the user from being injured if a piece of material is 'thrown' from the machine. An example of this is the cut/waste material from a lathe (see Figure 9.2). Many machines require guards by law.

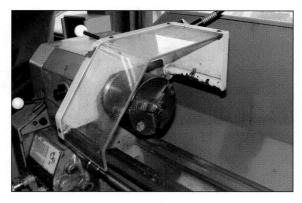

△ **Figure 9.2** Lathe guards

> **Activity**
>
> Identify the necessary checks you should take before using the following machinery:
>
> (a) pillar drill
>
> (b) fret saw
>
> (c) disc sander
>
> (d) wood lathe.

9.3 Appropriate dress – personal protective equipment (PPE)

Personal protective equipment (PPE) is specialist equipment to help protect a person undertaking a particular task. It includes the equipment listed in Table 9.1.

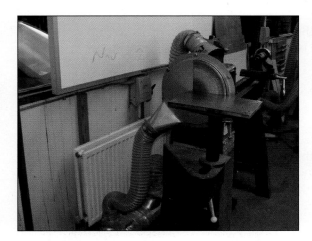

△ **Figure 9.1** Dust extraction on a disc sander

Item of PPE	Image	Used to ...	Example of machines/processes when it is required to wear the item of PPE
Safety goggles		protect the user's eyes	Pillar drill Lathe Belt sander Machine saw
Face mask		protect user from inhalation of dust and fumes	Using spray paint Disc sander
Visor		protect the user's eyes and face	Casting Welding
Apron		protect the user's clothes and skin	Pillar drill Lathe Belt sander Machine saw
Gaiters or leggings		protect the user's feet and legs	Casting Forging
Leather gloves		protect the user's hands and arms	Vacuum forming Casting

△ **Table 9.1** Personal protective equipment (PPE)

Contd

Item of PPE	Image	Used to ...	Example of machines/processes when it is required to wear the item of PPE
Ear defenders		protect the user's ears from loud noise	Machine saw
Rubber/plastic disposable gloves		protect the user's hands and skin	Using chemical adhesives Chemical etching
Hard hat		protect the user's head	When working on large items that may fall
Steel-capped shoes/boots		protect the user's feet	When using heavy objects

△ **Table 9.1** Personal protective equipment (PPE)

9.4 **Risk assessment and COSHH**

A risk assessment by workplaces, schools and public places is a legal requirement. It is a document that identifies possible risks that may occur in a situation and identifies precautions that can be put in place to reduce the likelihood of the risk. A risk assessment's purpose is to recognise the risk, identify the harm the risk could cause, consider what and how risks may occur, clarify measures that will be put in place to prevent the risks, and to give details of the emergency measures undertaken in the event of injury.

Control of Substances Hazardous to Health (COSHH) is a way of identifying the risks associated with specific substances. Examples that are used in school include resin, superglue, coolants and paints.

Each substance comes with its own material safety data sheet, which contains specific information about the safe use of the substance. The information includes how to handle the substance, what to do if you swallow or come into contact with the substance, how to deal with emergency situations such as spillages and how to dispose of the substance responsibly.

Key terms

Risk assessment – a document that identifies possible risks that may occur in a situation and identifies precautions that could be put in place to reduce the likelihood of the risks.

COSHH – a way of identifying the risks associated with specific substances.

Activity

Write a risk assessment for a pupil who is going to be undertaking the following tasks:

(a) pewter casting

(b) vacuum forming

(c) using the pillar drill.

9.5 Safety symbols in the workshop

There are many signs on display within a workshop. These signs are necessary to preserve your safety. You are required to be familiar with what they stand for and how to act in accordance with them (see Figure 9.3).

Mandatory signs are in blue. This means you must do what they say. Warning signs are displayed in black and yellow. Warnings of hazards are displayed in red diamond signs.

Controlled assessment link

When making products for your Controlled Assessment work, it is important to consider the health and safety issues covered in this chapter.

Wash your hands

Wear eye protection

Wear ear protection

HIGHLY FLAMMABLE

Corrosive

Toxic

Chemicals

△ **Figure 9.3** Safety signs

chapter 10
Safety for the consumer

⊙ Learning objectives

By the end of this chapter you should have developed a knowledge and understanding of:

○ how to ensure your product is safe for the consumer
○ the types of testing that can be undertaken during manufacture.

Introduction

When a new product is manufactured it is necessary for it to be safe for the consumer it is intended for. This chapter will focus on methods used to test a product during and after manufacture to ensure it is safe for the customer.

10.1 Quality control

Quality control is a process that is carried out during the manufacturing period to ensure that every product is manufactured to the standard of quality required. The quality of the product is checked after each manufacturing process and final quality tests are carried out once the product is complete.

Quality control during manufacture is made up of processes put in place to ensure each product is made to the same high quality as the previous one. Sometimes control devices are used. These include jigs, formers, templates and patterns.

A quality control manager will perform spot checks throughout the manufacturing process on random products to check that they are all made to the same standard. Any unsatisfactory products will be disposed of or recycled. The quality control manager will fill in a 'Certificate of Quality' form declaring his testing of a product at each stage of production.

If a product is mass or batch produced in large numbers it is very difficult to ensure every product is identical. During testing a quality control manager will allow 'tolerance'. Tolerance is a predetermined allowance for a product. For example, a square clock is manufactured to a design of 150 mm x 150 mm, but it may be agreed that it will pass the quality control check if it is between 145 mm x 155 mm.

Key term

Quality control – a process that ensures every product is manufactured to the highest standard possible.

Tolerance – the accepted limit of variation from product to product.

10.2 Quality assurance

Quality assurance is different to quality control as it does not test the quality of the final product but is a procedure to check the processes, people and systems who manufacture them.

A quality assurance manager will check the quality of the raw materials and components used in manufacture to ensure they are of the highest quality. The quality assurance manager will also check the machines used and the capability of the employees who are manufacturing the product, to ensure the product will be manufactured to the highest standard.

Activity

A batch of 20 key rings is to be manufactured out of card (see Figure 10.1).

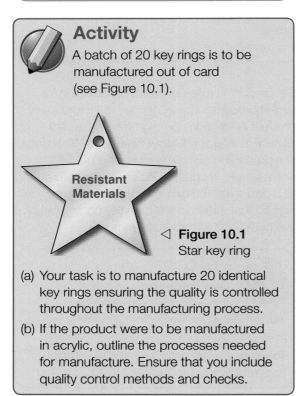

Resistant Materials

◁ **Figure 10.1**
Star key ring

(a) Your task is to manufacture 20 identical key rings ensuring the quality is controlled throughout the manufacturing process.

(b) If the product were to be manufactured in acrylic, outline the processes needed for manufacture. Ensure that you include quality control methods and checks.

10.3 Types of testing

There are different types of test that can be undertaken to test the product's suitability for the consumer's needs. The most common can be classified into three categories: quantitative testing, qualitative testing and sensory testing.

Quantitative testing

Quantitative testing produces data in numbers, for example the number of boys aged 13 who liked the latest computer game. The data can be used to make graphs and charts to represent the suitability of a product to the target market.

Qualitative testing

Qualitative testing produces data on opinions, normally in a verbal response, i.e. yes, no. For example, if you drop the game from a great height, will it break? What suggestions for improvement would you give to make the game better? Qualitative data are difficult to collate but are a very important test to ensure the suitability of a product to the consumer.

Sensory testing

Sensory testing is carried out by using the new product for a period of time then assessing its suitability. By doing this a designer can find out how suitable their product is when it is used by its targeted consumer group. This will provide important information on what the product is like to use, how safe it is and how useful it is.

10.4 Fair testing

Fair testing is important when testing any aspect of a product. A fair test means you are testing only one aspect at a time and ensuring that all of the test factors involved remain the same for each test. If you do not test a product under the same conditions then the testing is pointless as you will not know what outcome is the most effective.

Activity

Read the case studies below. Why are they not a fair test? What could Paul do to ensure the test is fair?

(a) Paul wanted to test the strength of his chair design to find out if it would hold 30 kg. He made three identical chairs, but all three were made out of different materials. He tested them by putting a 30 kg weight on them. For the first chair he dropped the weight onto the chair, for the second chair he carefully placed the weight down and on the third chair he pushed down as he placed the weight onto the chair.

(b) Paul wanted to see which material would be the best to make a toy parachute. He made three parachutes. One was bigger than the others. He then tested them by dropping them out of different windows from different heights.

10.5 Consumer groups

Key term

Consumer groups – independent associations and groups that test and compare products to make it easier for the customer to decide which product is best for them.

The Consumers' Association is responsible for the publication of the *Which?* magazine and website. The purpose of *Which?* is to test products and to compare products against other similar products to make it easier for the customer to decide which is best for them.

Activity

Go onto the internet and search www.which.co.uk. Use the website to compare offers on the latest:

(a) mobile phones

(b) children's car seats

(c) e-book readers.

Introduction

As technology develops, an increasing amount of machinery and equipment is being controlled by computer. Computer aided manufacture (CAM) has a range of advantages for designers and manufacturers and it is important that you understand these and can apply this knowledge to your own design work.

Many schools now have CAM systems that can be used during coursework. Some of the more commonly available variations are described here.

11.1 CAM systems

Vinyl cutter

This works in a similar way to a regular printer. Whereas a printer would move a print cartridge around some paper, a vinyl cutter moves a cutting blade around a sheet of material (paper, card or 'sticky backed' vinyl are most common). When the material is removed the cut sections can be taken out and the sheet is left with the pattern. These machines can cut complex 2D shapes that are drawn on computer aided design (CAD) software such as Techsoft 2D design and Adobe Illustrator.

△ **Figure 11.1** Cutting with vinyl

3D router

This is what is known as a subtractive manufacturing technique. This basically means that you start with a large block of material (these machines will cut MDF, hard and softwoods and some plastics such as thermosetting modelling resin and foam) and the tool removes the excess until your designed shape is left behind. These machines are quite expensive and require 3D CAD software in order to produce the three-dimensional models that the router requires to drive it.

There is a wide range of 3D CAD software available. Some of the more commonly used in schools are Pro/ENGINEER, Pro/DESKTOP, Solid Works and Autodesk AutoCAD.

△ 3D CAD software

△ **Figure 11.2** Boxford CNC Router

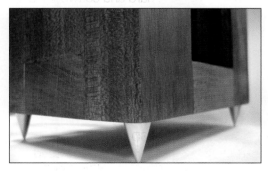

△ **Figure 11.3** Boxford CNC lathe and work produced on lathe (legs)

CNC lathe

This is the computer-controlled version of the traditional centre lathe. A centre lathe is used to manufacture turned parts in a range of metals and plastics. Various processes can be carried out with the tools within the machine, including turning down, parting off and drilling.

Laser cutter

More and more schools are seeing the benefit of this piece of equipment and they are becoming increasingly common. As with the vinyl cutter they require 2D CAD software to draw out the shapes or text to be cut from the sheet material. They can cut a wide range of materials, including some plastics, paper, card, fabrics, leather, wood veneers and MDF.

The machine uses the CAD file to control a small laser, which can vary in strength in order to cut through different thicknesses of material. One particularly useful aspect of this piece of equipment is that due to the power of the laser being variable, it can be used to engrave into the surface as well as cut all the way through. These laser cutters are so accurate that they can engrave a photographic image onto a sheet of material. Because the laser is essentially 'burning' through the material, however, it can give off toxic fumes and must be linked to an extractor.

Rapid prototyping system (RP)

Rapid prototyping allows very accurate 3D models of anything drawn in a 3D CAD program to be produced quickly. There are a number of types of RP machine, with each producing models in a different way. In each case the machine 'builds' the model in very thin slices or cross-sections. These manufacturing methods can be extremely expensive and the machines themselves often cost tens of thousands of pounds.

Stereo-lithography (or laser sintering) uses a laser beam to solidify slices of resin in a vat or layers of powder in a tray. The model is built up

from the bottom with a fresh layer of unhardened material laid down after each successive cross-section is solidified. The model is held in place by the material which has not been affected by the laser. On completion of the model this excess material can be cleaned away and reused on subsequent models.

3D printing works by building up layers of thermo-plastic, such as acrylic or ABS. It works a little bit like a regular printer but rather than a single layer of ink being laid onto the paper, multiple layers of plastic are built up onto the machine bed. On some machines a wax support material is used to hold the model as it is being built – this can be melted off afterwards.

△ **Figure 11.4** Spirit GE laser cutter and the results

◁ **Figure 11.6** An acrylic 3D printer

◁ **Figure 11.5** Rapid prototyping machine

◁ **Figure 11.7** GCSE project manufactured using these methods

Advantages and disadvantages of CAM

Advantages	Disadvantages
Quick	Expensive equipment
Can be run continuously 24/7	Requires CAD software
Multiple identical parts	Requires maintenance
Accurate	Puts skilled workers out of jobs
Can work in hostile environments	Training necessary to operate

△ **Table 11.1** Advantages and disadvantages of CAM

Activity

Consider the CAD systems mentioned. For each type, think of a way it could help produce part of or your entire GCSE project. Would the application of a CAM system improve your design?

11.2 Marking out

When beginning the manufacturing phase of your project it is important to mark out materials accurately. There is a vast range of tools designed to make this job as easy and accurate as possible. Table 11.2 should allow you to choose the most appropriate tool for your job.

Tool	Image	Description	Can be used on ...
Rule		Long piece of material (usually steel or plastic) with measurements marked along the edge	wood, metal, plastic, card
Try-square		A right-angled tool that allows perfect 90° angles to be marked or checked	wood, metal, plastic

△ **Table 11.2** Tools for marking out and their uses

Contd

Tool	Image	Description	Can be used on ...
Engineer's square		The same as a try-square but more accurate	wood, metal, plastic
Marking gauge		Allows parallel lines to be marked along the edge of a piece of material	wood
Compass		Holds a pen or pencil and allows circles of any radius to be marked on the material	wood, paper, card
Centre punch		Used with a hammer or mallet to mark a single point for drilling or holding a compass	metal
Spring dividers		Similar to a compass, with two points for marking hard materials	metal, plastic

△ **Table 11.2** Tools for marking out and their uses

Contd

Tool	Image	Description	Can be used on ...
Adjustable bevel		Works in the same way as a try-square although angles other than 90° can be set	wood, metal, plastic
Vernier callipers		Uses a sliding section over a steel bar (marked with fractions of millimetres) to measure distances with great accuracy (around 0.02 mm)	metal, plastic
Micrometer		Uses a screw thread which when tightened onto a piece of material can measure the distance with an accuracy of 0.01 mm	metal, plastic

△ **Table 11.2** Tools for marking out and their uses

Tolerance

When drawing or measuring a part or product it is necessary to include a tolerance. A tolerance is a numerical value with upper and lower limits (a margin of error). It is usually noted as 10 mm ± 0.02 mm. This would indicate that the part could be anywhere between 9.98 mm and 10.02 mm.

Tolerances become very important when two or more parts have to fit into or around other parts. This is especially true if the parts are being manufactured by different people, different companies or even in different countries.

Joining wood

Wood is used in a wide range of applications and each calls for careful consideration of the joining method. There are pros and cons to each method and it is important that you have a good working knowledge of these in order to make sound decisions.

Wood joints can be used to create a strong and visually appealing corner on wooden products. Each type of joint varies in strength, difficulty to manufacture and visual appearance. All of these factors should be taken into consideration when selecting an appropriate joint.

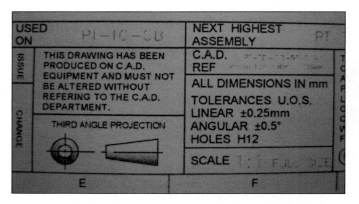

USED ON	PI-IC-CB	NEXT HIGHEST ASSEMBLY	PT	
ISSUE	THIS DRAWING HAS BEEN PRODUCED ON C.A.D. EQUIPMENT AND MUST NOT BE ALTERED WITHOUT REFERING TO THE C.A.D. DEPARTMENT.	C.A.D. REF		
		ALL DIMENSIONS IN mm	
CHANGE	THIRD ANGLE PROJECTION	TOLERANCES U.O.S. LINEAR ±0.25mm ANGULAR ±0.5° HOLES H12	
		SCALE 1:1 FULL SIZE	
E		F	

△ **Figure 11.8** Manufacturing specifications must include a tolerance

Activities

1. You are provided with a strip of pine 600 mm × 50 mm × 15 mm. Using notes and sketches, show how this could be marked out to produce a frame 180 mm × 130 mm.

2. On the drawing in Figure 11.9, show that the steel rod has been manufactured to be between 3.3 mm and 3.7 mm.

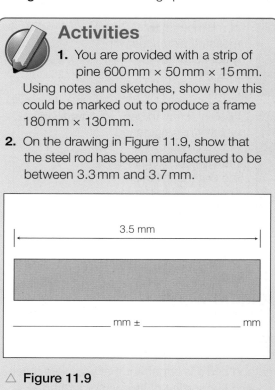

3.5 mm

_____ mm ± _____ mm

△ **Figure 11.9**

3. An aluminium bar has been cut to 1005 mm ± 0.05 mm. What are the maximum and minimum dimensions it can be?

Butt joint

◁ **Figure 11.10**
A butt joint

This is the simplest but also the weakest of the frame joints. It is usually made permanent through the use of an adhesive such as PVA or using nails.

Dowelled joint

◁ **Figure 11.11**
A dowelled joint

A dowelled joint is similar to a butt joint but it is strengthened through the addition of drilled holes with dowels glued into them.

Mortise and tenon joint

These are more complex to make than the previous joints, although the resulting joint is stronger and more stable. They involve the end of one of the timbers being shaped and narrowed in order to fit snugly into a hole that is cut into the other piece of timber.

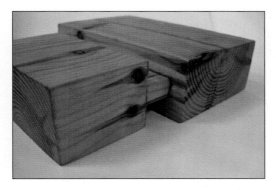

△ **Figure 11.12** A mortise and tenon joint

Comb or box joint

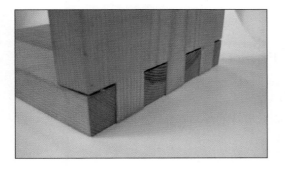

△ **Figure 11.13** A comb or box joint

This joint requires more accuracy during the marking out and cutting phase, which results in a more difficult joint to produce, although the increased surface area gives a much stronger joint. The interlocking 'fingers' also give an appealing look to this joint.

Dovetail joint

◁ **Figure 11.14**
A dovetail joint

Although similar to the comb joint, the shape of the dovetails means that it is both stronger and more difficult to produce. These joints are often found on high-quality furniture manufactured by skilled craftsmen. Figure 11.15 shows a GCSE product incorporating various joints.

◁ **Figure 11.15** Using joints at GCSE

Joining metal

When joining metal permanently to another piece of metal, a process using heat is generally the best option. The three methods described here are soldering, brazing and welding. Each of these methods is suitable for specific tasks and it is therefore vital that you understand the differences fully and can make informed decisions when selecting the most appropriate one.

Soldering

The most common use for this method of joining metal is in electronic circuitry. Small amounts of 'solder' (an alloy of tin, silver and copper) are melted using a soldering iron across the point where the two electronic components meet (see Figure 11.17). The same principle is applied when soldering sheet materials. The solder melts at a relatively low temperature, typically around 180°C.

Soldering is used on copper, tin and brass and should be considered as an option only if the strength of the joint is not a priority as it is the weakest of the joining methods.

Brazing

This works in a similar way to soldering, although it works in a significantly higher temperature range (around 870°C). Brazing is used to join mild steel and uses a filler rod that is brought just

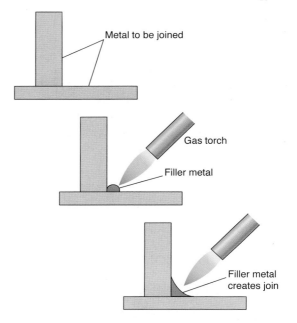

Metal to be joined

Gas torch

Filler metal

Filler metal creates join

△ **Figure 11.18** The brazing process

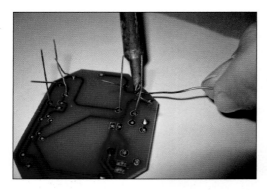

△ **Figure 11.17** Soldering circuitry

Activity

For the following products, name a suitable joint and give a reason:

(a) drawer front on an expensive unit

(b) picture frame

(c) supports between chair legs and frame.

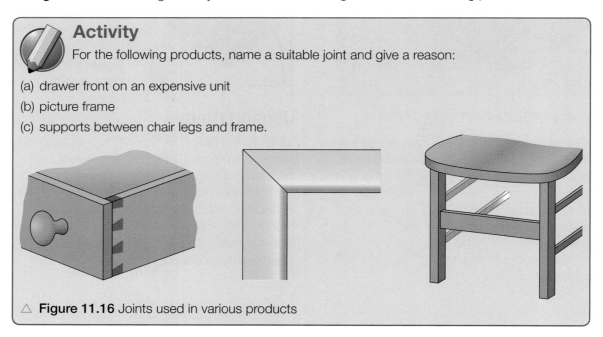

△ **Figure 11.16** Joints used in various products

above its melting point and allowed to flow into the join between the two materials (see Figure 11.18). Flux is also used to aid this flow and to protect the join from oxidisation.

It is vital to ensure that the join is completely clean; this can be done with emery cloth. The filler rod is then heated using a gas torch (commonly oxy-acetylene).

Welding

Welding comes in a variety of forms (see Figure 11.19). The two most common in schools are oxy-acetylene gas torch and electric arc. Other methods include tungsten inert gas (TIG), metal inert gas (MIG), spot and seam.

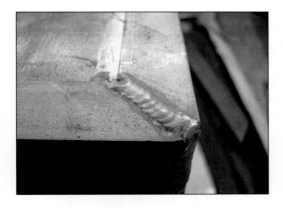

△ **Figure 11.19** Example of welded parts

All forms of welding use heat to 'fuse' together the parts to be joined. Welding is typically the strongest form of joining metal with heat.

Oxy-acetylene welding uses the same torch as brazing but is required to work at a much higher temperature (2500°C). As the flame comes into contact with the join the metal edges melt and fuse with one another. A filler rod can be added at this point to increase the strength of the joint.

Electric arc welding uses a spark passing across a gap in the torch to generate the heat required to melt the metal. Again a filler rod is used to increase the strength of the joint.

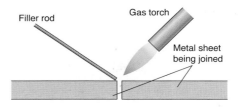

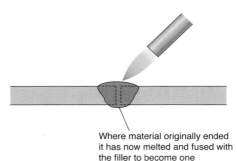

Where material originally ended it has now melted and fused with the filler to become one

△ **Figure 11.20** The welding process

11.3 **Tools**

Tools can be split into two major categories – hand and power. Hand tools are the traditional tools that have been around for hundreds of years without changing a great deal. Power tools are the evolution of the more traditional hand tools using electricity to physically move parts of the tool at speed. Power tools can make working with materials easier and quicker.

Hand tools

Saws

There is a wide variety of saws for different applications. In school the most commonly found types are:

o coping saw – this has a thin blade and wide frame to allow curves to be cut into the material – suitable for plastic and wood
o junior hacksaw – this has a smaller frame than the coping saw with a thicker blade and smaller teeth; the thicker blades will cut in straight lines more easily than curves – suitable for metal and plastic

- hacksaw – this is a larger version of the junior hacksaw – suitable for metal and plastic
- tenon saw – this uses a deep blade with a reinforcing bar across the top; the coarse teeth and solid blade make it ideal for cutting timber panels and planks into pieces – suitable for wood
- panel saw – this uses a long, deep blade similar to that on the tenon saw, although there is no reinforcing bar, making it easier to cut larger sheets of material – suitable for wood.

Shaping tools

Once you have cut your material to size with the appropriate saw there are numerous shaping tools to help form the material to your desired shape.

- Files – these are made up of a handle and a steel shaft covered in small, sharp teeth. There is a range of profile shapes that allow you to 'fit' the file into different shapes on your piece of work. Files can be used on metal, plastic and, in some cases, wood.
- Planes – these use an angled blade held in a frame to remove thin layers of wood from the edge of a panel.

Activity

Using notes and sketches, describe how hand tools can be used to produce a five-sided MDF box like that shown in Figure 11.21.

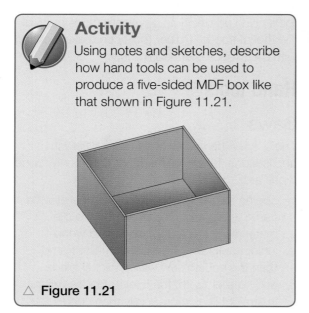

△ **Figure 11.21**

△ **Figure 11.22** Files, planes and chisels

- Chisels – these use a sharpened, shaped shaft to cut away sections of timber. They can be struck with a mallet in order to remove the material.

Drills

These are used to create holes in your material. The drill uses interchangeable 'bits', which come in a range of sizes and styles for different materials. The bit is held in place by a chuck, which is tightened with a chuck key.

△ **Figure 11.23** Getting to grips with a drill

Power tools

Pillar drill

As with the regular drill these rotate a drill bit against a piece of material in order to cut a hole through it. Pillar drills are fixed to a tall frame with a 'bed' onto which you can clamp your work. The chuck and drill bit are then lowered to the work piece using a handle mechanism.

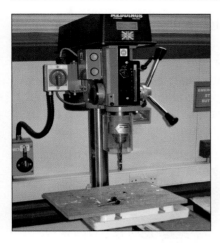

△ **Figure 11.24** Pillar drill

Belt sander/linisher

This piece of equipment uses two spinning cylinders with a belt of abrasive cloth stretched between them. Your piece of material can then be placed against the rapidly moving belt to remove material quickly.

◁ **Figure 11.25** Belt sander/ linisher

Lathe

There are two varieties of lathe commonly found in schools – centre lathe and wood lathe. Both machines work by holding a piece of material and turning material while a range of tools is held against the work to remove layers until the desired cylindrical or conical shape is formed.

△ **Figure 11.26** Lathe

Band saw

This works like a large pulley system. Two wheels are used to stretch a steel, belt-shaped blade so that when one of the wheels is turned by the motor the belt is forced to move, allowing large pieces of material to be cut easily by the teeth. These are particularly dangerous and should be used only by people with appropriate training.

Belts with different types of teeth are available for cutting different materials.

△ **Figure 11.27** Band saw

Scroll saw

These saws use similar blades to those found on a coping saw. They can be used to cut intricate shapes due to the narrow blade. Some machines have a variable speed at which the blade reciprocates.

△ **Figure 11.28** Scroll saw

Milling machine

This machine uses a fluted cutting tool to remove material accurately from a block of material by moving the machine bed. The bed can be moved in three directions (side to side – X axis, front to back – Y axis, and up and down – Z axis) using rotating levers. These machines can also be controlled by a computer (CNC).

△ **Figure 11.29** Milling machine

Hand-held power tools

Cordless drill

These use batteries to allow the drill to be hand held and easily portable. The battery can usually be recharged and is placed low down in the handle to give better balance while in use.

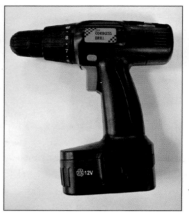

◁ **Figure 11.30** Cordless drill

Jigsaw

These saws use a reciprocating blade held on the bottom of the tool to cut curved shapes. These can either be mains powered or use a rechargeable battery.

△ **Figure 11.31** Jigsaw

Router

These tools are commonly used to give a finished edge to wood or to cut slots. A special cutting tool is fixed on the underside of the tool and can be used in conjunction with a guide to give accuracy.

△ **Figure 11.32** Router

 Activity

List all the health and safety checks that should be carried out on a:

(a) pillar drill

(b) linisher

(c) lathe.

11.4 **Working with metal**

Casting

Casting is the general term given to melting a material and pouring it into a mould. The most common material to be cast is metal and many schools have access to pewter casting equipment.

Pewter melts at just over 200°C and this makes it an easy entry into the world of forging (see below). Moulds can be made in a variety of ways, including CNC routers, hand tools and laser cutters (see Figure 11.33).

i) The design for the part to be cast has been cut into the surface of the material using a CAM router. A back panel which is flat or that also has a design engraved can be placed on to the first, creating a hollow mould. It is important that a small funnel (sprue) is also cut into one edge to allow the molten metal to be poured in.

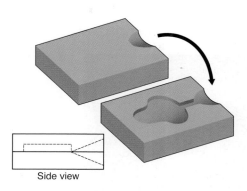

Side view

ii) + iii) If a CAM router is unavailable then the same process can be carried out using a three-part mould. The central piece of material is cut by hand or using a laser cutter to the desired shape (again leaving an open sprue in one end for the molten metal to be poured in). Blanking plates are sandwiched around this , creating a hollow mould to be cast into.

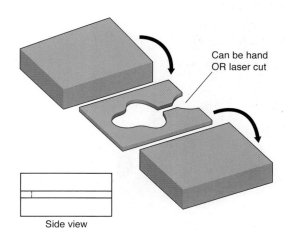

Can be hand OR laser cut

Side view

△ **Figure 11.33** Options for mould making

Pewter is heated to a liquid state and poured carefully into the mould. Specific school casting equipment such as the Flamefast unit (see Figure 11.34) makes this significantly easier than the more traditional method of heating the pewter in a crucible using a gas torch. The arms of the lamp in Figure 11.35 illustrates cast parts.

△ **Figure 11.34** Flamefast unit

△ **Figure 11.35** Cast arms on a GCSE lamp

Forging

This process involves heating metal (usually steel) in a forge (a very hot fire with air blown in to increase the temperature further) to a point where it becomes soft enough to be hammered into a shape. Traditionally this hammering action was carried out by hand, but industrial versions of this process are now carried out by powered hammers and presses.

△ **Figure 11.36** A forge

Cold forming

Soft or thin metals (copper, aluminium and brass) can be formed while cold, although the hammering action can cause them to become hard and brittle. This is known as work hardening and can be overcome by the application of heat (annealing).

△ **Figure 11.37** Hammering metal sheet can result in metals becoming hard and brittle

Cold working

Sheet metals can be folded and rolled using jigs and formers. It is important to measure accurately and cut out the 'net' (see Figure 11.38) of your shape to be folded carefully (see Figure 11.39). It can be beneficial to make a card prototype first.

△ **Figure 11.38** Card net

△ **Figure 11.39** Folded sheet steel

Press forming

Sheet metal can be 'stamped' into a 3D shape using this process. This can add rigidity and allow interesting shapes to be created. This process is used regularly in the motor industry to produce car body panels.

Activity
Draw up a four-step guide to the process of press forming. Use notes and sketches in your answer.

11.5 **Moulding plastic**

Plastic is a very versatile material. Due to its ability to be formed into complex shapes it is now used in many everyday products. Plastic is divided into two families – thermoplastic and thermosetting plastic. In school, thermoplastics are more commonly used due to their ability to be heated and formed easily (and reheated if necessary).

There is a wide variety of forming techniques for plastic, each with its own advantages. It is likely that in your school you will have access to a few different methods of forming plastic as they are a great way of manufacturing parts for your major project. Many schools will have line benders, vacuum formers and sometimes even injection moulders.

Line bending

The most simple way of forming a thermoplastic is folding a sheet of the material. This is done using a line bender (sometimes known as a strip heater, see Figure 11.40). This piece of equipment uses a length of wire that is heated with supports either side to hold the sheet of plastic. The plastic will become soft along the line that is closest to the wire and can then be folded to the desired angle. Jigs can be used to produce multiple pieces of the same angle or if a precise angle is required (see Figure 11.41).

Depending on the thickness of the plastic sheet, it may be necessary to heat both sides of the fold line. You will also need to take care not to overheat the plastic as this can cause blistering.

△ **Figure 11.40** Line bender

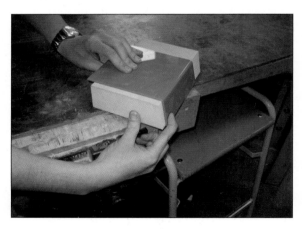

△ **Figure 11.41** Using a jig

Vacuum forming

Vacuum forming is widely used in the food packaging industry for producing hollow tubs and pots such as for yoghurt (see Figure 11.42). The process allows the production of open-ended, hollow shapes which are limited in their complexity so as to allow the mould to be removed from the plastic afterwards.

△ **Figure 11.42** Vacuum former

Most sheet thermoplastics can be used in a vacuum former, although HIPS (high-impact polystyrene) is most commonly used in school. The plastic is clamped between a heater and a mould. When the plastic is softened the mould is raised up into the plastic and all of the air in the cavity is pumped out, allowing the air pressure to force the soft plastic to fit closely against the mould (see Figure 11.43).

The design of the mould is critical – it must incorporate a draft angle (the mould must get wider towards the base, see Figure 11.44). If it has overhangs or the draft angle is insufficient, the mould can get 'locked' inside the formed plastic.

The mould can be manufactured from MDF or natural timber. Figure 11.45 shows a radio with vac-formed casing. In industry the mould would be made from stainless steel or aluminium as they are more durable and can be reused many thousands of times.

Injection moulding

This process is occasionally used in some schools for very small parts (see Figure 11.46). The process is more commonly found in industry as it becomes cost effective only when producing many

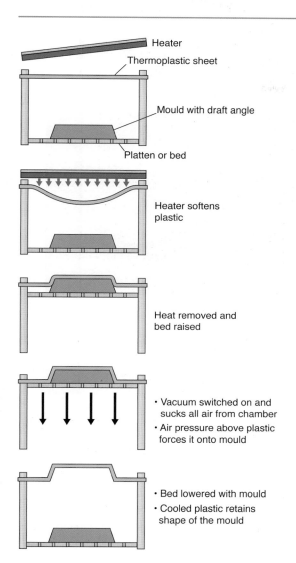

Heater

Thermoplastic sheet

Mould with draft angle

Platten or bed

Heater softens plastic

Heat removed and bed raised

- Vacuum switched on and sucks all air from chamber
- Air pressure above plastic forces it onto mould

- Bed lowered with mould
- Cooled plastic retains shape of the mould

△ **Figure 11.43** The vac form process

△ **Figure 11.44** Mould and draft angle

△ **Figure 11.45** GCSE radio with vac formed casing

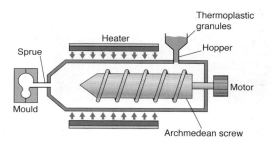

Thermoplastic granules

Heater

Sprue

Hopper

Motor

Mould

Archmedean screw

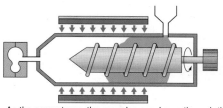

As the screw turns, the granules are drawn through the heated chamber and melt

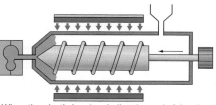

When the plastic has 'pooled' at the end of the chamber, it is forced under pressure into the mould through the sprue

△ **Figure 11.46** Moulding step by step

thousands of parts. The moulds used in industry can cost tens of thousands of pounds and are generally made from stainless steel (see Figure 11.47). Each part manufactured from the mould will use only a few pence worth of plastic.

◁ **Figure 11.47** School injection moulder

Activity

Practise sketching the process for vacuum forming and for injection moulding. You should be able to describe all of the necessary steps using sketches and annotations.

11.6 **Forming wood**

Laminating wood veneers

It is possible to create curved wooden surfaces using a similar technique to that which is used to create plywood. Plywood is simply very thin wood veneers layered up with adhesive. This has two main benefits – added strength through the alternation of the grain in the veneers and the ability to create much larger sheet materials that could not be produced naturally from a tree.

The curve in the sheet is created using a former, such as the one in Figure 11.48. These formers are typically block materials that have been cut in two with the desired curve.

△ **Figure 11.48** MDF former

A former can be created easily using layers of MDF to create a thick block. Then, using a band saw, the curve can be cut through the block and smoothed with glass paper. The veneers of timber may need to be soaked in water for around 24 hours prior to being clamped into the former if the curve is particularly tight or complex. This will allow a little more flex and once the veneers have dried out in the former they will retain the curved shape. PVA glue can now be applied between the veneers (three layers are adequate) and the veneers returned to the former until the adhesive dries.

◁ **Figure 11.49** Laminated GCSE radio

Turning

This process involves a rotating block of timber that is shaped using specialist tools. The spinning motion allows the production of cylindrical and conical parts as well as bowl shapes when using the face plate.

△ **Figure 11.50** The components for turning

Traditionally lathes have been used to produce chair legs, spindles and posts, but they can be very useful when producing parts for more modern products such as iPod docks (see Figure 11.51).

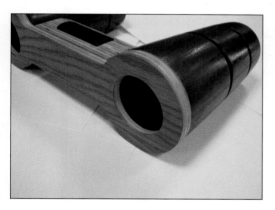

△ **Figure 11.51** GCSE iPod dock

Quantity production

Wherever products are being produced there are scales of production (Table 11.3). These scales can range from 'one-off' bespoke pieces to 'mass-produced' electronic components produced in their millions.

In school it is often necessary to manufacture a number of pieces to the same specification. In order to do this, some industrial techniques can be applied.

Jigs

Jigs work by holding the material in the same position every time for a repeatable process such as drilling. This saves time and increases accuracy by cutting out the human error when measuring each part. Jigs can also be used when line bending thermoplastic or folding sheet metal. This allows the same angle to be created every time (see Figure 11.52).

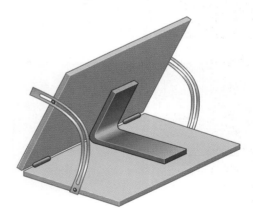

△ **Figure 11.52** Bending jig

Templates

These are simple paper items fixed to a block of material (see Figure 11.53). They can then be used to cut around. A good way to produce accurate templates is to draw your parts in CAD and print out a full-scale image.

One-off	This is when a single item is produced, often at the request of a client with specific requirements. These products are mainly made by hand and take a long time to manufacture. This makes it very expensive.	Bespoke furniture, skyscraper, wedding cake
Batch	This is when a set number of items is produced and repeated if required. In order that each item is identical it is often useful to produce jigs, formers and templates. The number produced in each 'batch' can vary greatly, from 10 to 1000.	Books, loaves of bread, clothing
Mass	This is when tens of thousands of items are produced. In order to manufacture at this scale it is likely that an automated system is employed and the steps of manufacture are broken down into sections of an assembly line. Processes such as injection moulding become economically viable at this level. Due to the automation of much of the process, unskilled labour can be recruited at a lower cost than the skilled workers required for one-off and batch.	Cars, light bulbs, toothbrushes
Continuous	This level of production runs 24 hours per day, 7 days per week. Because of this the entire system will be computer controlled, with very little human input required. Manufacturing costs can be reduced massively through the reduction of staff and the efficiency of a machine that has only one job to do.	Matches, paper, steel

△ **Table 11.3** Scales of production

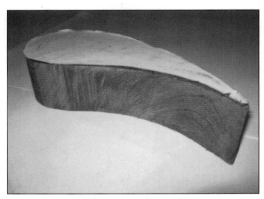

△ **Figure 11.53** Paper template stuck to a block

Activity

Research what other products are made using each of the four scales of production and generate a list, including reasons for this choice.

Introduction

When designing products it is important to consider the ways in which materials can be joined together. A sound knowledge of these techniques will give you greater freedom when coming up with your ideas. It will ensure that when you come to manufacture your design you produce a quality product. Incorporating the use of CAM into your work and understanding how these systems can give greater freedom to your creative thoughts can allow you to realise some fantastic products. It is also really important to understand what finishes are available and how to apply them – the finish of your work can make a massive difference.

This chapter deals with ways in which materials can be joined together, how CAM can be used during manufacture, and how to select appropriate finishes and apply them to your product.

12.1 Permanent methods of joining materials

When joining materials it is important to consider whether you want them to come apart again at any time. If the parts never need to be separated, you should choose a permanent fixing.

A permanent joint can be created using adhesives, heat, mechanical fixings or by physically cutting the materials (wood joints).

Adhesives

Adhesives come in a multitude of forms. Each has its own properties which make it suitable for certain materials and applications. It is very important to choose the right adhesive for your joint.

PVA (polyvinyl acetate)

This is often referred to as wood glue. It is white in colour, then dries clear. PVA has excellent strength properties when fixing wood to wood (often stronger than the wood itself) but is unsuitable for use with plastics or metal. PVA has a number of

△ **Figure 12.1** Gluing a timber frame

limitations: it is not waterproof and has a drying time of a few hours. You should take these into consideration when selecting PVA.

Solvent cement

This adhesive can be used on a range of thermoplastics. It works by melting the surfaces of the two materials and allowing them to fuse together. Acrylic is commonly joined in this way along with HIPS (high impact polystyrene) and PVC (polyvinyl chloride).

△ **Figure 12.2** Cementing acrylic

Super glue (cyanoacrylate)

Super glue will bond a range of materials together (including your fingers!). It is extremely fast acting and primarily used for plastics. The fumes from super glue are toxic and it should not be used for long periods of time in enclosed spaces.

Araldite (epoxy resin)

This is a two-part adhesive (a thermosetting resin and a hardener). When mixed in equal quantities the resin and hardener react and set, leaving a very strong joint. This adhesive is available in 'fast setting' or 'slow setting' forms and will bond a variety of materials, including wood, metal, ceramic and most plastics. Epoxy adhesives are so strong they are used to attach the wings to aircraft.

Hot melt glue

This is a fairly weak glue that is used with a glue gun. The gun heats up and melts a stick of thermoplastic which is then pumped from the gun onto the surface to be joined. The glue cools and sets very quickly. It can be useful when making quick models or prototypes.

△ **Figure 12.3** Using super glue

Heat processing

Metals can be joined permanently with heat in two ways – brazing and welding. When selecting which method to use, you should consider the strength of join required and how closely the materials fit to one another.

Brazing

Brazing (Figure 12.4) involves joining two close-fitting metals by melting a 'filler metal' near the join. Capillary action draws the molten metal between the two surfaces to be joined and when cooled the joint is formed. It is really important that the two metals to be joined are exceptionally clean and that there is very little gap between the surfaces. The filler metal should have a lower melting point (usually between 450°C and 1000°C) than the two to be joined. Flux can be used on the join to keep the joint clean and allow the filler metal to flow into the join more easily. Soldering is a type of brazing that works at lower temperatures (around 200°C).

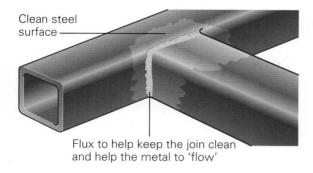

Clean steel surface

Flux to help keep the join clean and help the metal to 'flow'

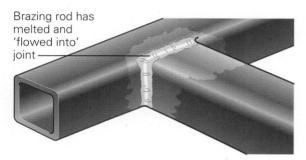

Brazing rod has melted and 'flowed into' joint

△ **Figure 12.4** Brazing two close-fitting metals

Welding

Welding involves melting two metals together to form a strong, permanent fixing. There is no need for the filler metal as in brazing, although it can be used to make the joint even stronger. Welding can be carried out with a hot flame (oxy-acetylene torch welding) or a hot spark (electric arc welding).

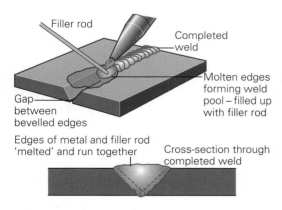

Filler rod

Completed weld

Molten edges forming weld pool – filled up with filler rod

Gap between bevelled edges

Edges of metal and filler rod 'melted' and run together

Cross-section through completed weld

△ **Figure 12.5** Welding leaves a strong, permanent fixing

Mechanical fixings

Mechanical fixings are a useful method of joining thin sheet materials. The strength of the fixing depends on the properties of the materials being joined. There is no need for any chemical reactions or melting to take place, although the fixings are generally visible on the product so this should be taken into consideration in your design work.

Rivets

When selecting rivets as a method of joining your materials you will need to drill holes through both sheets to be joined. A rivet works by being passed through the hole until its head is against one side of the join; the other side is then flattened to stop it passing back through the hole. With this style of rivet it is necessary to have access to both sides of the join. If this is not the case and you can get at only one side, a special type of rivet can be used, called a 'pop' rivet.

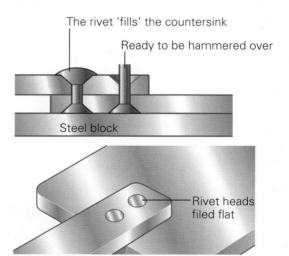

The rivet 'fills' the countersink

Ready to be hammered over

Steel block

Rivet heads filed flat

△ **Figure 12.6** Using rivets

Nails

Nails are pin-shaped pieces of steel that are driven through one piece of material into another to be joined. Nails are used commonly to join wood and are forced through using a hammer or nail gun. It is the friction between the nail and the wood that holds the joint together. They are quick to use, although they can split the timber occasionally when using hardwoods. In this instance you can drill a pilot hole, which will prevent this.

Frame joints

Frame joints (Table 12.1) can be used to create a strong and visually appealing corner on wooden products. Each type of joint varies in strength, difficulty to manufacture and visual appearance. All of these factors should be taken into consideration when selecting an appropriate joint.

Wood joint	Image	Pros	Cons
Butt		Easy to manufacture	Relatively weak
Dowel		Easy to manufacture	Fairly weak (although stronger than a butt joint)
Mortise and tenon		Very strong	More difficult to manufacture, although specialist machinery can be used

△ **Table 12.1** The various frame joints

Contd

Wood joint	Image	Pros	Cons
Comb/box/finger		Interesting visual feature at the join, strong	Precise measurement and marking out necessary to achieve good-quality finish
Dovetail		Excellent aesthetic value, extremely strong	Very difficult to manufacture accurately

△ **Table 12.1** The various frame joints

12.2 **Temporary methods of joining materials**

On some occasions it is useful to have a joint that can be separated whenever necessary. This could be for a variety of reasons, such as maintenance or ability to be transported easily. This type of fixing is typically a mechanical component (see page 140).

Screws

Screws come in a variety of shapes and styles. They all have a wide head, smooth shank, long core and a thread circulating around the core. Most screws require a clearance hole to be drilled into one of the pieces of timber that is slightly wider than the shank. A pilot hole needs to be drilled into the other piece of wood that is slightly smaller than the core.

Self-tapping screws are manufactured from hardened steel and have a sharpened thread that cuts into the material as it passes through it. (See pages 142–143 for more information).

◁ **Figure 12.8**
Getting down to the nuts and bolts

◁ **Figure 12.7**
Screwing an access panel

Nuts and bolts

Nuts and bolts are used to hold together parts. The bolt has an external thread fully or partially covering the cylindrical shaft; at one end there is a head, which is available in a number of shapes for different purposes. Most commonly the head is hexagonal so that it can be gripped with a spanner. The nut is manufactured with an internal thread, which matches that on the bolt so that they can be fastened together.

When a nut and bolt are being used to fasten together parts clearance holes (slightly larger than the thread of the bolt) are drilled in the parts for the bolt to pass through and the nut is fitted to the opposite side and tightened to secure the parts together.

Knock down fixings

Knock down (KD) fixings are commonly found in flat-pack furniture and are designed to allow easy assembly with minimal tools in the customer's home. There is a variety of KD fixings, including plastic block connectors, cam screw and nut, corner plates and chipboard fasteners.

△ **Figure 12.9** KD fittings for easy assembly

 Key term

Flat-pack furniture – furniture supplied as a kit of parts that the buyer has to assemble.

Student Exemplar

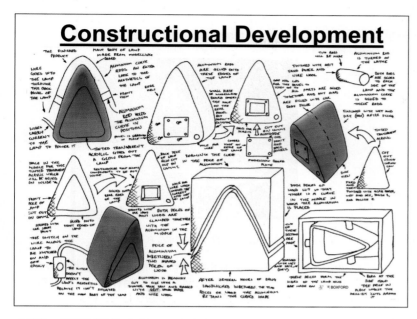

△ **Figure 12.10** Development for manufacture

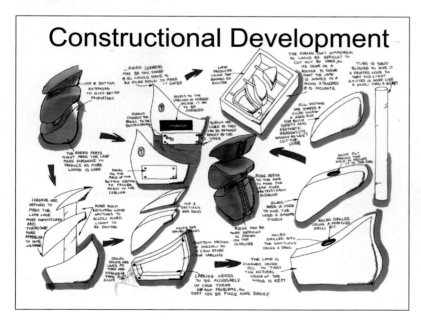

△ **Figure 12.11** Development for manufacture

137

Activity

For the list of items below, identify the most appropriate method for joining the highlighted sections:

(a) mahogany drawer fronts on expensive bedside cabinet

(b) aluminium wings onto jumbo jet

(c) steel car body panels onto chassis

(d) chipboard flat-pack wardrobe panels

(e) brake levers onto a bike's handlebars

(f) ABS casing on a games console.

12.3 CAM systems

Computer aided manufacture (CAM) is the use of electronic machinery to produce a physical part or product. CAM is controlled by a computer aided design system, a computer program that allows the designer to generate a 2D or 3D model of their idea.

There is a wide range of CAM systems, which vary in their method of manufacture and can be split into two main groups: additive and subtractive.

△ **Figure 12.12** Modelling parts with Pro/ENGINEER

Additive

These machines mainly consist of rapid prototypers. These pieces of equipment use a variety of methods to 'build' a three-dimensional model of a CAD drawing. They are basically 3D printers. Car manufacturers often use rapid prototypers to produce scale models, which they can then test in wind tunnels.

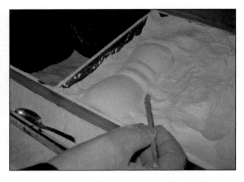

△ **Figure 12.13** Getting a 3D view

The methods these machines use to build the models include those listed below.

○ Selective laser sintering (SLS) – using a laser to harden powdered material one layer at a time. As each layer is hardened, fresh powder is laid down over the previous and the process continues.

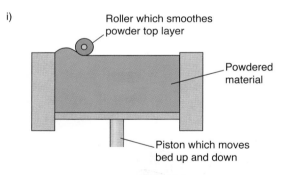

i)

Roller which smoothes powder top layer

Powdered material

Piston which moves bed up and down

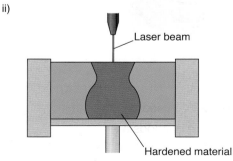

ii)

Laser beam

Hardened material

△ **Figure 12.14** Selective laser sintering

o Stereolithography (SLA) – using a laser to harden a liquid resin one layer at a time. The resin is contained in a large vat. When the laser has finished, the remaining liquid can be drained and the 3D model removed.

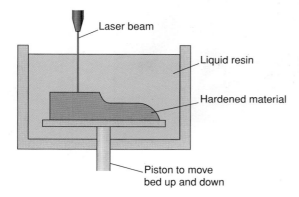

△ **Figure 12.15** Stereolithography

o Fused deposition modelling (FDM) – a fine nozzle is used to 'pump' out plastic material and build, one layer at a time, a solid model of a CAD drawing. The nozzle is able to move freely in all directions and is heated to allow the material to be melted sufficiently to stick to the rest of the model.

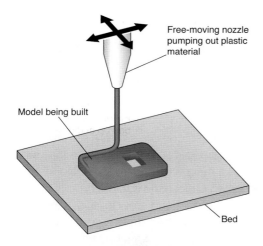

△ **Figure 12.16** Fused deposition modelling

All of the above methods are extremely accurate and allow a designer to quickly produce parts and prototypes for testing – and on some occasions produce finished items.

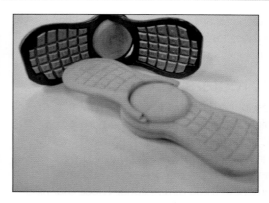

△ **Figure 12.17** Selection of GCSE projects manufactured using CAM

Subtractive

These machines start with a block of your chosen material and remove all of the material that is unnecessary – similar to a sculptor producing a statue from a block of marble.

△ **Figure 12.18** Using subtractive machines

139

The machines are computer-controlled versions of the more traditional human-controlled tools. They include those described below.

CNC routers

Just as in the more traditional version of this machine a rotating tool is moved across the block, removing material as it goes. The CAM version is controlled by using data from a CAD drawing, which the machine converts into movement in three dimensions. These machines can be used with wood and specialist modelling plastics.

CNC lathes

Again, this machine works in the same way as the traditional version but controlled by data from a CAD file produced by the designer. The lathe rotates the block of material at high speed while a computer-controlled tool is passed along it to create the conical/cylindrical shape required by the designer.

Student Exemplar

△ **Figure 12.19** Student practical outcome manufactured using subtractive methods

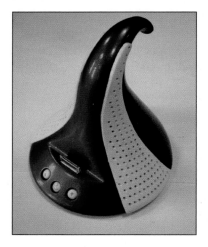

△ **Figure 12.20** Student practical outcome manufactured using additive methods

Activity

Consider computer aided manufacture and how this has affected the way in which designers work in industry. What are the benefits and drawbacks of the process?

12.4 **Pre-manufactured components**

Pre-manufactured components include parts like nails, screws, nuts and bolts, hinges, stays and handles. These parts are designed to be used by lots of different companies making different products.

Pre-manufactured components are sometimes called 'standard parts'. This is because they are available in a range of standard sizes. Normally a designer will choose the size of part that is needed in a product and allow for this in the design. If a standard part is not available in the correct size, the design might be changed slightly to allow the closest standard size to be used.

Most products assembled from resistant materials use pre-manufactured components. The parts are bought from a supplier rather than made by the company making the finished product. This is because if a company had to make just a few of them, they would be very expensive. However, because the company that makes the pre-manufactured parts might make millions of them, it can use mass production techniques to make them at a very low cost.

Nails

There are several different types of nail, which are used for different jobs. These are available in a range of standard lengths. Most nails are made from low carbon steel. However, nails made from galvanised (zinc-coated) steel or phosphate-coated steel, brass and copper are also available.

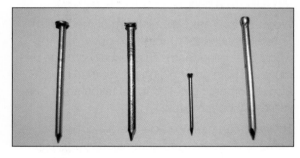

△ **Figure 12.21** Common types of nail

Round wire nails

Round wire nails are used for general joinery work. Typically, they are available in lengths from 12 mm to 150 mm.

Oval wire nails

Oval wire nails are used for interior joinery, such as furniture. They have virtually no head. This means that they can be punched into the material and filler can be used to hide them. They are available in lengths from 12 mm to 150 mm.

When using oval wire nails, it is important that they are driven into the wood along the grain. If this is not done, their shape may split the wood.

Panel pins

These are used to pin thin sheet material or for small-scale work. They are available in lengths from 9 mm to 25 mm.

Hardboard pins

These are used to attach hardboard to frames. In many ways they are similar to panel pins. However, because of the pointed head they do not need to be punched below the surface of the wood.

Masonry nails

Masonry nails are used to fasten objects into concrete, brickwork or mortar. There are three different types: round, square and fluted. However, they should not be used where high strength is required. Typically, they are available in lengths from 12 mm to 254 mm.

Annular nails

These are used to attach objects to plasterboard and internal drywall panels. They have sharp ridges all along the nail shaft. This provides greater holding power than a smooth nail.

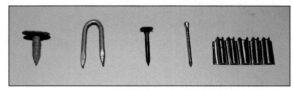

△ **Figure 12.22** Common types of fastener

Clout nails

These are used to fasten roofing felt to shed roofs. They have a wide head to prevent the felt from splitting. They are normally galvanised to prevent rusting.

Staples

Staples are used to attach upholstery to furniture. They are also used to make packing crates and pallets. Round staples are normally hammered into the wood. Square types of staple can be fired from a staple gun. This means they can be put in place very quickly, reducing the time needed to make the joint.

Cut tacks

These are also used to attach upholstery to furniture. They are normally hidden when in use.

Corrugated fasteners

These are used to make quick and cheap corner joints and wooden frames. They are hammered into the material spanning across each joint.

△ **Figure 12.23** Frame with corrugated fasteners in each corner

Key term

Fastener – a part used to attach two or more other parts together.

Nailing techniques

When making a frame using nails, where the nails are placed affects the strength of the joint. The nail positions should be staggered to avoid splitting the wood along the grain. If the nails are hammered into the wood at a slight angle (rather than always straight down), this will make the joint stronger and more difficult to pull apart. This is known as dovetail nailing.

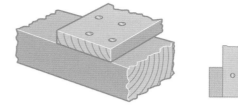

△ **Figure 12.24** Staggered nailing

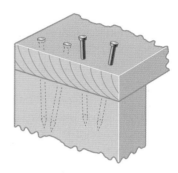

△ **Figure 12.25** Dovetail nailing

Wood screws

Wood screws are a simple form of mechanism. This is because they are driven down into the wood by turning them. They usually provide more strength and holding power than nails. Also, if something needs to be taken apart, they can easily be removed.

They are commonly made of steel or brass. Some steel screws are galvanised to improve their corrosion resistance when used outdoors. They may also be chrome plated to improve their appearance. Brass screws are softer than steel. Care must be taken when using them with woods that are hard, such as oak and teak, to avoid them snapping.

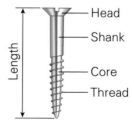

△ **Figure 12.26** Parts of a wood screw

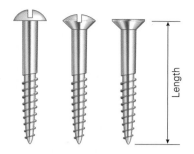

△ **Figure 12.27** Length of a wood screw

There are several types of wood screw, which are used for different applications. These are commonly available with three types of slot in the head: straight slot, Phillips and posidriv (Figure 12.29). The straight slot allows the greatest turning force to be applied. However, the Phillips or posidriv slot types mean that the tip of the screwdriver is less likely to slip out and damage the surface of the wood. It is also easier to locate the head of the screwdriver into a Phillips or posidriv slot when using automated machines.

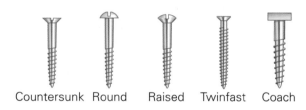

Countersunk Round Raised Twinfast Coach

△ **Figure 12.28** Common types of wood screw

Straight slot Phillips Pozidriv

△ **Figure 12.29** Types of slots in screws

Countersunk head

Using a screw with a countersunk head means that the head of the screw can be level with, or slightly below, the surface being joined. This means the joint can be made to be flat.

Round head

Round head screws are used to fasten thin materials to wood. For example, this could be metal or plastic sheet. The area under the head spreads the pressure applied across the sheet material.

Raised head

Raised head screws are used for decorative purposes. For example, this might include attaching the handle to a door.

Twinfast

Twinfast screws are used on chipboard. They have a coarse (bigger) thread that provides greater holding power.

Coach screw

A coach screw has a square head and is tightened with a spanner, not a screwdriver. It is used where great holding power is required. For example, coaches might be used to attach the main supporting beam of a tree house to a tree, or to fasten metalwork vices to benches.

Screw sizes

Screws are available in a wide range of standard sizes. In the UK, their size is often defined by a description such as M8. The number after the M is the maximum diameter of the screw, which is known as the gauge. This might be followed by another number to tell you the length of the screw. This means that an M8 × 20 screw has a gauge of 8 mm diameter and a length of 20 mm.

The size of the thread on the screw is known as its pitch. This is related to its gauge and is specified by a standard such as BS3643, ISO261 or ISO965. This means that two screws with the same description should always have a thread of the same size.

Using screws

When using screws it is normal to drill a pilot hole. This helps to stop the wood from splitting. For example, preparing to screw together two pieces of wood with a counter sunk screw involves:

1. drilling a pilot hole to the diameter of the core of the screw

2. drilling a clearance hole slightly larger than the diameter of the shank

3. drilling the counter-sink for the head to sit in.

To improve the appearance of the finished product, often the screw is covered with a cap or cup. This is better than covering the screw with filler as it allows the screw to be removed at a later date if necessary. There are several different types of caps and cups. These may push onto, screw into or position under the screw head.

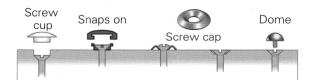

△ **Figure 12.31** Caps and cups

Machine screws, nuts and bolts

These are used to make temporary joints. They can be taken apart using a screwdriver, spanner or Allen key.

Machine screws

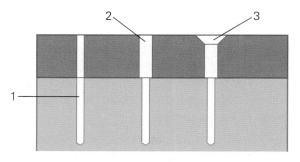

△ **Figure 12.30** Preparing two pieces of wood to be screwed together with countersunk screws

Machine screws are available in a wide variety of lengths, diameters and types of head. The head may have a slot for a screwdriver or a socket for an Allen key. The advantage of using an Allen key is that considerable force can be applied without the danger of the tool slipping out.

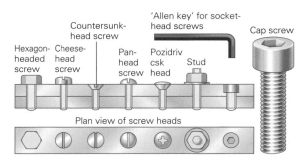

△ **Figure 12.32** Types of machine screw

Self-tapping screws

Self-tapping screws are made from hardened steel. They cut their own thread as they are screwed into the material. They are normally used to join thin sheet material, such as metal or plastic.

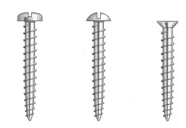

△ **Figure 12.33** Three types of self-tapping screw

Bolts

Bolts are made from high-strength steel. They may have either a square or hexagonal head, and are normally tightened using a spanner. The length of the bolt is measured from underneath the head to the end of the bolt. There may be a small shank or the thread may go along the length of the bolt, when it is known as a set screw.

△ **Figure 12.34** A hexagonal head bolt

Nuts

Similar to bolts, most nuts have square or hexagonal heads. These are tightened using a spanner. However, wing nuts are specially shaped to allow them be tightened using the fingers. When in use, vibration can cause the nut to loosen, weakening the joint. To reduce the risk of this happening, lock nuts can be used. To eliminate the risk completely, a castle nut can be used with a split pin.

| Wing nut | Hexagonal nut | Square nut | Locking nut | Castle nut and split pin | Nylon (fibre lock) nut |

△ **Figure 12.35** Six types of nut

Washer

Washers help to protect the surface on which the bolt or nut is being tightened. They spread the load and help to prevent the loosening due to vibration.

| Plain washer | Lock washer | Grover spring washer | Spring washer | Tab washer | Serrated washer |

△ **Figure 12.36** Common types of washer

Knock-down fittings

Most flat-pack furniture includes knock-down (KD) fittings. KD fittings allow the furniture to be assembled easily using basic tools, such as a screwdriver, hammer and mallet. There is a wide variety of KD fittings available, to meet the needs of different types of joint in the furniture. It is important to recognise that flat-pack furniture does not only include KD fittings – it also often uses permanent joints, such as dowels.

One-piece corner blocks

One-piece corner blocks are used to join together the sides of the cabinet, from the inside. These are normally made from plastic but can be made from wood.

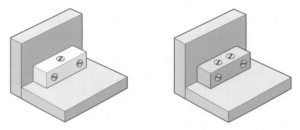

△ **Figure 12.37** One-piece corner blocks made from plastic and wood

Rigid joints

A rigid joint is made from a single piece of moulded plastic. This is often held in place by four screws. This carries out the same task as a one-piece corner block.

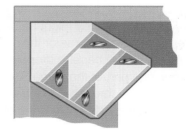

△ **Figure 12.38** Rigid joint

Two-piece corner blocks

Two-piece corner blocks are also used to make cabinets. They are often used where access for tools might be limited. One block is attached to each side of the cabinet. Pins are used to locate the two blocks together. A bolt is then used to fasten the two parts together.

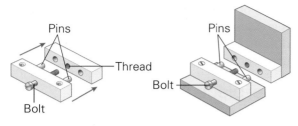

△ **Figure 12.39** Two-piece plastic corner block

An alternative design of the two-piece corner block does not include location pins. However, the parts are located when the final screw is inserted into preformed holes in the plastic moulding.

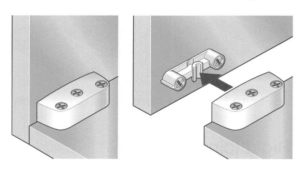

△ **Figure 12.40** Alternative design of two-piece plastic corner block

Scan fittings

Scan fittings are often used to join frames together. For example, they might be used to attach the legs to a bed frame or the sides to a cabinet. An aluminium barrel is dropped into a hole drilled in one part of the frame. The barrel has a threaded hole through its centre. An Allen screw is pushed through a hole in the other part

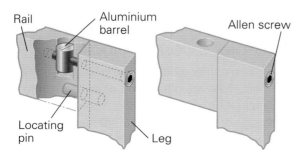

△ **Figure 12.41** Scan fitting

of the frame and screwed into the barrel. This pulls the joint together. Sometimes a locating pin is used to help align the two parts.

Cam lock

Cam locks are used to attach the front to the sides of a drawer. A threaded rod is screwed into the inside of the drawer front. The circular cam lock is dropped into a hole in the drawer side. When a screwdriver is used to turn the cam lock, this pulls the drawer front towards it, tightening the joint.

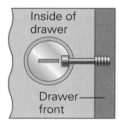
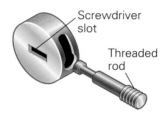

△ **Figure 12.42** Cam lock

Leg fastening

Leg fastenings can be used to attach the legs to a piece of furniture or to reinforce a structure. A common design involves using a rod with screw threads at each end. One end of the rod screws into the leg. The other end passes through a connecting steel plate, onto which a nut is tightened.

△ **Figure 12.43** Two types of leg fastening

Hinges and stays

Hinges and stays are used to support parts that swing open, such as doors, windows and the tops of boxes. Fitting hinges requires a lot of care and skill, otherwise the parts will not line up.

Butt hinge

Butt hinges are one of the most common types of hinge. They are often made from steel or brass. To improve the appearance of the joint, they are usually recessed into the edge of the wood.

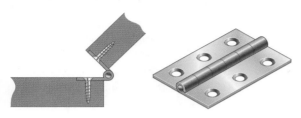

△ **Figure 12.44** Butt hinge

Back-flap hinge

Back-flap hinges are used for joints in large products. For example, this might include the flaps (leaves) on tables or large lids on boxes. They have more surface area than butt hinges, which provides greater strength. In addition the staggered position of the holes makes it less likely to split the grain of the wood.

△ **Figure 12.45** Back-flap hinge

Piano hinge

Piano hinges are used where a lot of support is needed along the edges of a long product. For

△ **Figure 12.46** Piano hinge

example, they are used to attach the cover over the keys of a piano or to attach the top to a case for a snooker cue.

Tee hinge

Tee hinges are used on gates and sheds. The long arm provides great support.

△ **Figure 12.47** Tee hinge

Flush hinge

Flush hinges are used for small products, such as attaching lids to small boxes. They are mounted on the surface of the wood and one flap fits inside the other when it is closed. Compared with a butt hinge, the advantage of a flush hinge is that it does not need to be recessed into the wood.

△ **Figure 12.48** Flush hinge

Concealed hinge

Concealed hinges are often used in kitchen cabinets. They are normally adjustable, which means that the door can easily be moved up or down, or in and out, to ensure that it is in the right place.

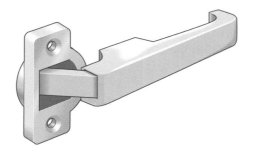

△ **Figure 12.49** Concealed hinge

Stay

Stays are a type of hinge. They are used to connect two parts of a cabinet, such as a flap that opens out. They are attached with screws to the inside of the cabinet and to the part that opens out.

Stays are often made from steel or brass. They may include adjustable resistance to opening. This means they can be made to open with little force, or they can be made to need a large force to open.

◁ **Figure 12.50** Brass stay with adjustable resistance

Catches, locks, handles and runners

These are essential components to ensure the smooth operation of doors and drawers. Catches, locks and handles are often referred to as 'door furniture'.

Ball catch

Catches help to ensure that doors are held shut. Ball catches do this by providing a mechanical resistance to opening or closing. They can be recessed in the door and frame so that they are hardly noticeable. They are available in a wide range of sizes, from the small catches used in cabinets to the large catches used for the internal doors in a house.

△ **Figure 12.51** Ball catch

Spring catch

Spring catches give very positive fastening. However, they tend to be unattractive in appearance. They are often used for products where they are hidden, such as inside the doors of wardrobes.

△ **Figure 12.52** Spring catch

Magnetic catch

Magnetic catches are often used in kitchen cabinets. The magnet is usually attached to the inside of the cabinet and the plate to the door. They are available with covers made from a variety of materials, ranging from white plastic to brass.

◁ **Figure 12.53** Magnetic catch

Locks

The purpose of a lock is to hold a door or lid closed. The difference between a lock and a catch is that a catch can be 'released' with a simple pull on the door or lid, but a lock needs an extra action to release it. There are many different types of lock, which cover a wide range of purposes.

Hasp and staple

A hasp and staple is often used with a padlock to fasten shed doors or gates.

△ **Figure 12.54** Hasp and staple

Toggle catch

Technically, this is a catch rather than a lock. However, they are often used as locks. For example, they are used to attach the top and bottom parts of a toolbox together and keep it closed.

△ **Figure 12.55** Toggle catch

Box-style cupboard catch

This type of lock is used on cabinets and cupboards. There are many variations of this design available.

△ **Figure 12.56** Box-style cupboard catch

Handles

The handle, or 'pull', allows you to open and close a door or drawer easily. It can also make a significant difference to the appearance of a product. A wide range of different types of handle is available. Many of these are attached using screws from the inside face of the door or drawer.

Runners

Many items of furniture contain drawers. There are several ways that a drawer can be supported. If we think about the bedside cabinet shown in Figure 12.58, it could be supported by a shelf underneath it. However, this would

149

| Beech | Polished brass | Anodised aluminium | Oak | Chromed finish |

△ **Figure 12.57** A selection of drawer and cabinet handles

use more materials, increase the weight and the cost, and a method of attaching the shelf would be needed.

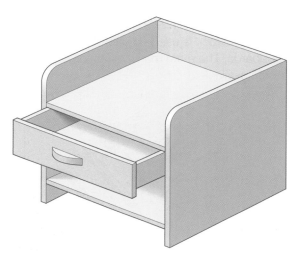

△ **Figure 12.58** Bedside cabinet

One way of supporting the drawer is to make grooves in the sides of the drawer. These could be supported on strips added to the inside of the

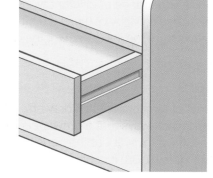

△ **Figure 12.59** Groove to support drawer

cabinet. The strips could be pinned and glued in position. The disadvantage of this approach is that the drawer may be difficult to pull out due to friction, especially if it is heavy.

An alternative solution is to buy a pair of drawer runners, as shown in Figure 12.60. The two part As are screwed to the inside of the cabinet. The part Bs are screwed to the side of the drawer. When in use, part B slides in and out of part A. Often part B includes wheels to allow easy movement, and part A contains a stop, which prevents the drawer being pulled out too far.

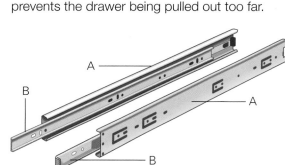

△ **Figure 12.60** Drawer runners

Rivets

Rivets are available in several forms.

- Round head rivets, also known as snap head rivets, are used where it does not matter if the top of the rivet sits slightly higher than the material.
- Countersunk head rivets are used where the top of the rivet must be flush with the surface being joined.
- Flathead rivets are used in thin material where it is not possible to make a countersink.

o Bifurcated rivets are used to join soft material, such as plastic or leather.

Round head (snap head)   Flathead   Countersunk   Bifurcated

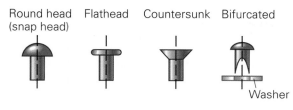

Washer

△ **Figure 12.61** Types of rivet

An advantage of riveting over other joining techniques is that it can be used to join dissimilar materials together. However, you need to be able to work from both sides of the joint and the material being joined must not be damaged by the hammering over of the rivet.

Pop riveting

Pop riveting was developed for use when building aircraft. It is used to join the thin sheets of aluminium that are used to make the body skin of aeroplanes.

A pop rivet has a hollow body with a steel pin running through it. The steel pin has an enlarged head at the end of the rivet. As for solid rivets, the first steps in the process of pop riveting involve making an overlap in the sheet metal to be joined and drilling a hole. The pop rivet is held in a rivet gun. It is pushed into the hole and the gun is squeezed. This pulls the steel pin, causing the enlarged pin head to expand the head of the rivet. When the correct pressure is reached, the pin breaks off. This leaves the formed rivet with the pinhead in it.

Compared with using solid rivets, the advantage of pop riveting is that you need to get to only one side of the parts being joined. However, because the rivets are hollow, they are not as strong as solid rivets.

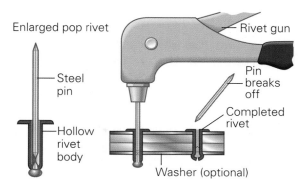

Enlarged pop rivet — Rivet gun — Steel pin — Pin breaks off — Hollow rivet body — Completed rivet — Washer (optional)

△ **Figure 12.62** Pop riveting

Activities

1. Carry out a product analysis of an item of flat-pack furniture.
Identify the pre-manufactured components used.

2. You have been asked to design a cupboard for use in a teenager's bedroom. Your design should include at least one door and at least two drawers. Sketch a design, using labels to indicate where pre-manufactured components would be used.

3. Using the internet, gather information about pre-manufactured components from companies that sell them. Create a table listing:

o the different types of pre-manufactured components
o the materials they are made from
o the sizes they are available in
o how much they cost.

12.5 Preparation of materials and the application of a finish

For the three main categories of materials (wood, metal and plastic) it is important that the correct preparation is applied to the surface in order to achieve a good finish.

Wood

There are two main ways to achieve a flat surface on the raw edge of a piece of timber: using a sander (see Figure 12.63) or a plane (see Figure 12.64).

A plane uses a sharp blade housed inside a steel body to shave thin layers of material from the edge as it is passed over. The finish achieved with a plane, when used by a trained craftsman, is excellent, although in an untrained hand it is easy to make a mess of your work. A belt or disc sander is an easier alternative to a plane, although the finish is less precise.

◁ **Figure 12.63** Sander in action

△ **Figure 12.64** Plane in action

Glass paper

Various grades of glass paper can be used after the edge has been taken down to the required level with the tools just mentioned, to achieve a better finish. When using glass paper you should always start with the roughest/coarsest grade and work down towards the smoothest/finest. Try to follow the grain of the wood as far as possible as this will achieve a better finish.

Glass paper grades are numbered, with higher numbers being finer (60, 80, 150, 240, etc.).

△ **Figure 12.65** Make the grade with glass paper

Metal

After metal has been cut it can often have 'burrs' (short, sharp metal shards) along the edge. These can be removed through draw filing (see Figure 12.66). After draw filing, the surface can be smoothed and cleaned further using emery cloth (similar to glass paper although backed with fabric) followed by wet and dry paper (silicon carbide paper). This is available in a series of grades (coarse to fine) – the higher the number, the finer the grit: 400, 800, 1000, etc. If the metal has been coated in oil to prevent corrosion, this should be cleaned off with white spirit prior to any finish being applied.

△ **Figure 12.66** Draw filing

Plastic

Plastic, if moulded, will usually have a perfect finish and will have been manufactured in the appropriate colour. If the edges have been trimmed and are therefore rough, the same procedures as used for metal to remove burrs and smooth down can be applied.

△ **Figure 12.67** Achieve the perfect finish with plastic

Applying appropriate finishes

The last stage of any manufacturing process is the finish. Selecting the correct finish and applying it well can make a huge difference to the appearance of your work. Finishes are used to both alter the appearance of a material and protect it against a variety of threats.

Wood

It is important to apply a finish to wood in order to protect its surface as it can become dented and scuffed when in regular use. Selection of a suitable finish can minimise this. It is also possible to bring out the natural beauty of the grain with application of the right finish.

Wax

Wax can be used to add an attractive shine to a piece of timber. The wax is rubbed into the surface with a clean cloth. Due to the oily nature of the wax it also adds a degree of waterproofing. After the wax is applied it can be buffed with a soft, clean cloth to achieve a high-shine finish (Figure 12.68).

△ **Figure 12.68** Wax can give a high-shine finish

Oil

A variety of oils are available, including teak and linseed. The oil can be applied with a cloth or brush and will provide a deep shine that increases with additional coats. As with wax, the oil will provide some waterproofing and will increase the toughness of the wood surface.

△ **Figure 12.69** Oil gives a deep shine

Stain

This finish is designed solely to change the colour of wood. It is semi-transparent and allows the natural grain of the timber to show through. However, it does not give any protection.

Varnish

Varnish is applied with a brush and will give an excellent, high-shine finish. Polyurethane varnish, which is one of the varieties available, will also give excellent protection when dried as it forms a plastic coating over the surface of the material.

△ **Figure 12.70** Varnish gives shine and protection

Paint

Paint comes in a variety of types. Water-, oil- and solvent-based paints are available, and each has its own application. If a non-toxic finish is required then water-based paints are the obvious choice as they are completely harmless, although the finish is less hard wearing. Oil-based paints will give a longer-lasting finish and a deeper shine but are much more labour intensive to apply (undercoats and primer are necessary).

Paint can be mixed to any colour and as such it is a popular choice when a 'natural' look is not required. Water- and oil-based paints can be applied with brushes, sponges and rags to achieve a good finish. Solvent-based paints are generally sold in an aerosol can so that they can be sprayed on directly.

◁ **Figure 12.71** Paint gives you plenty of choice

Metal

Applied finishes on metal are especially important to ensure that corrosion of the material is minimised.

Paint

When applying paint to metal it is very important to apply a primer coat, which will give the material a 'key' to stick to. Solvent-based paints (aerosol cans) are the popular choice as they can achieve an excellent finish quickly without the use of brushes.

Cellulose-based paints can be applied with a brush or through an aerosol, and give excellent weather protection for outdoor use.

Plastic dip coating

This process gives a coating of polythene to the metal item. Heating the metal to around 200°C and inserting it into a chamber containing the powdered polythene allows the powder to melt onto the surface. This chamber is known as a fluidising bath. Once completed and cooled the surface has a softer feel, making it ideal for children's playground equipment frames.

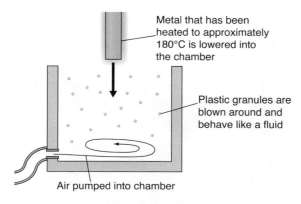

Metal that has been heated to approximately 180°C is lowered into the chamber

Plastic granules are blown around and behave like a fluid

Air pumped into chamber

△ **Figure 12.72** Fluidising bath

Anodising

This process is used to toughen the surface and improve the wear resistance of some metals, most commonly aluminium. The process uses an electric current passing through an electrolytic solution from the part to be treated, to a negative cathode. As the current flows from the part that

△ **Figure 12.73** Anodising: suitable for mountain bikes

is serving as a positive anode to the negative cathode aluminium oxide builds up on the surface of the part and creates the anodised finish. Dyes can be added to create coloured parts.

Hot dip zinc coating

This process is used to stop corrosion (rusting) on steel and iron parts. The part to be protected is dipped into a vat of molten zinc and when removed this coating oxidises and creates a dull grey finish that has excellent rust resistance. Items that have been through this process can be seen readily all around us; for example outdoor railings, crash barriers and constructional materials are all everyday items that require great corrosion resistance due to their outdoor life.

Electroplating

This process allows a metal part to be covered in a very thin layer of another metal to increase a desired property, for example better wear resistance or corrosion resistance. The process works by connecting the metal to be plated to the negative terminal of a power source and the material to coat the part is connected to the positive terminal. Both parts are then submerged in an electrolytic liquid. As the current flows from the positive material to the negative part the donor metal is oxidised and dissolves; it then flows through the solution and coats the surface of the item in question.

Plastic

In industry plastic does not always require finishing. The plastic is coloured during the manufacturing process and, on removal from the mould or die, it has a perfect finish.

In school, plastics such as acrylic are often finished using polish after being prepared with files and wet and dry paper. This is because the forming techniques used in school are rarely as accurate as those used in industry. In school it is unlikely that you will have the luxury of manufacturing your own plastic so it may be necessary to change the colour of the plastic after manufacture rather than before, as in industry. It is possible to apply a painted finish to the plastic surface; in this instance a coat of primer could be necessary to help the paint to adhere to the plastic.

◁ **Figure 12.74** Plastic: for the perfect finish

Student Exemplar

△ **Figure 12.75** Finished practical outcome

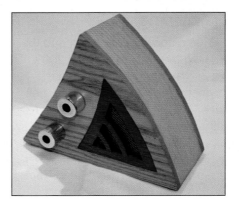

△ **Figure 12.76** Finished practical outcome

△ **Figure 12.77** Finished practical outcome

Activity

For each of the items listed below, name a suitable finish and give a reason why it is suitable:

○ pine dining room table
○ aluminium bike brake lever
○ ABS TV remote
○ front door of a house
○ steel body panel from a car.

chapter 13
Systems and control

Learning objectives

By the end of this chapter you should have developed a knowledge and understanding of:

○ a range of basic mechanisms and electrical systems
○ how to put in place quality checks and procedures during the making of a product
○ the use of jigs and fixtures during the manufacture of products.

Introduction

In GCSE Resistant Materials, systems are used in two ways:

○ **many products include simple systems made from moving parts, or simple electrical circuits; these allow the product to do much more than a design that does not include them**
○ **when making products, instructions and procedures are used to ensure that a product is good quality.**

This chapter describes several basic mechanisms and electrical systems that are often used in GCSE Resistant Materials projects. It explains how quality checks and procedures are implemented during the manufacture of a product, and how simple devices can be used to make sure that manufactured products are of a consistent quality.

Systems can be classified as two types: hard and soft. Both types are used in GCSE Resistant Materials, but they are very different in what they are used for.

A 'hard' system is made from physical parts. These work together to carry out a task. For example, this could be the switch used to make the light come on when you open a fridge door. Hard systems are important because they allow a product to do something useful that a piece of material on its own could not do. In GCSE Resistant Materials, they are made from basic mechanisms or electrical systems.

A 'soft' system is a method or procedure that is used to control an activity. This could be instructions on how to check a product to make sure that it is correct, or a procedure for evacuating the building if there is a fire. Soft systems are normally instructions that are used by people. In GCSE Resistant Materials, we are mainly concerned with quality control systems.

13.1 Types of system

Key terms

System – either a group of parts that works together to carry out a task, or a method or procedure used to control an activity.

Mechanism – a device or machine that changes movement in some way.

Key term

Quality control systems – checking a part after a process to make sure that it is right.

13.2 **Mechanisms**

A mechanism is a device or machine that changes movement in some way. It normally changes the direction of movement or the amount of movement.

One of the most common mechanisms is a screw, which is used to join two pieces of wood together. As it is turned by a screwdriver, it moves deeper into the wood. Similarly, to make the jaws of an engineer's vice move closer together, you turn the bar at the end.

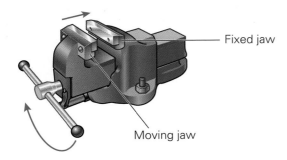

Fixed jaw

Moving jaw

△ **Figure 13.1** Engineer's vice

Most mechanisms are made from combinations of basic components: levers, linkages, pulley and belt, chain and sprockets, gears and cams.

Levers

A lever moves around a fixed point, called a pivot. They are often used to increase force. A pair of scissors consists of two levers, pivoting about the point where they are joined.

Linkages

Linkages are widely used in mechanisms. They can transfer force and change the direction of movement. They are easy to identify as they will have at least one fixed pivot point and at least two other pivot points. The fixed pivot point does not move. The other pivot points will connect parts of the linkage together but can move position compared with the fixed pivot.

A reverse linkage reverses the direction of movement. These are often used in the frames of collapsible devices, such as pushchairs.

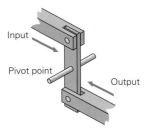

Input

Pivot point

Output

Reverse motion linkage

△ **Figure 13.2** Reverse linkage

A parallel motion linkage is used where you want to transmit movement in the same direction, but you cannot do this in a straight line. This type of linkage is used for the moveable drawers on a metal tool box.

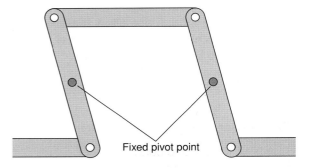

Fixed pivot point

△ **Figure 13.3** Parallel motion linkage

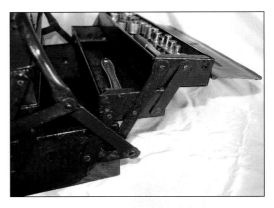

△ **Figure 13.4** Metal toolbox with trays using a parallel motion linkage

A bell crank linkage changes the direction of movement by 90°. These are used for the brake mechanisms on a bicycle.

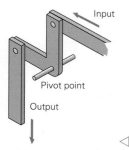

Bell crank linkage

◁ **Figure 13.5** Bell crank linkage

◁ **Figure 13.6** Bell crank linkage used for a bicycle brake mechanism

Pulley and belt

Belt drives are used to connect rotating parts. In its most simple form, the belt might be a smooth piece of material looped tightly between two wheels. This type of arrangement is used in workshop machines like the pillar drill.

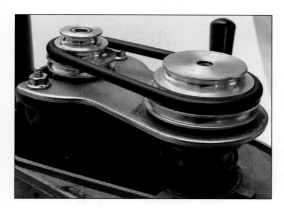

△ **Figure 13.7** Belt drive

In a simple belt drive, the belt might slip or slide over one of the wheels. This might mean that not all the movement is transferred.

Chain and sprockets

A chain and sprocket has teeth in the sprocket that fit into gaps in the chain. This helps to prevent slippage. Chains and sprockets are used in bicycles and motorbikes.

△ **Figure 13.8** Bicycle chain

Gears

Similar to belt drives and the chain and sprockets, gears are used to connect rotating parts. Compared with chains and sprockets they allow more force to be transmitted.

The simplest form of gear is called a spur gear. These look like toothed wheels that interlock. A set of gears joining two points in a mechanism is called a gear train.

If only two spur gears are used in a gear train, the direction of turning is reversed. If a third gear is added, it will move in the same direction as the first gear.

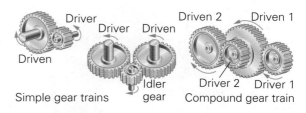

△ **Figure 13.9** Simple gear trains

Another form of gear is called the bevel gear. Here the teeth are at an angle. They can be used to change the direction of the rotary movement, so that instead of being in line with the first gear it is at an angle. For example, in a hand-powered 'egg beater' drill, the user turns a vertical wheel on the side of the drill. The gears change this into the horizontal motion of the drill bit.

A rack and pinion looks like a spur gear attached to a line of teeth. This is used to change rotary movement into side-to-side movement. These are often used in steering systems, to move the wheels from side to side when the steering wheel is turned.

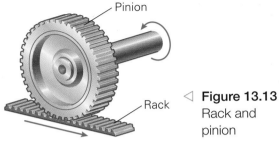

△ **Figure 13.10** Bevel gears and worm gear

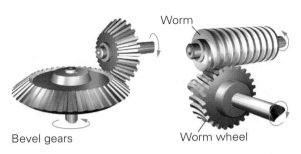

◁ **Figure 13.13** Rack and pinion

△ **Figure 13.11** Double pinion drill

A worm gear can be used to change the direction of rotary movement by 90°. These are often used to drive the wheels in small robot buggies.

Cams

Cams are used to change rotary movement into up-and-down movement. The cam is a rotating shape. A 'follower' follows the shape of the cam as it rotates. The amount of up-and-down movement depends on the shape of the cam.

Eccentric cam with plain follower

Pear shaped cam with roller follower

Snail cam with plain follower

△ **Figure 13.14** Types of cam

△ **Figure 13.12** Worm gear in a robot buggy

◁ **Figure 13.15** Cam used in a moving toy

13.3 **Electrical systems**

Electrical systems range from simple lamp circuits to complicated alarm systems. They can include a wide range of electrical components, as shown in Table 13.1. When these are drawn as electrical circuits, the components are represented by symbols. Lines are used to show the connections between components.

Component	Symbol	What it looks like	What it does
Cell			Provides power for the circuit
Battery			
Voltage rail	9V o— 0V o—		
Resistor			Limits the amount of electrical current, fixed value
Variable resistor			Limits the amount of electrical current, variable value
Potentiometer			
Thermistor			Changes the resistance of the circuit as the temperature changes
Light-dependent resistor			Changes the resistance of the circuit as the amount of light changes

△ **Table 13.1** Electrical components

Contd

Component	Symbol	What it looks like	What it does
Capacitor			Stores electrical charge
Push to make switch			Turns the circuit on or off
Push to break switch			
Single pole single throw switch			
Buzzer			Turns electricity into sound
Loudspeaker			
Bell			
Buzzer			
Microphone			Turns sound into an electrical signal
Lamp			Turns electricity into light

△ **Table 13.1** Electrical components

Contd

Component	Symbol	What it looks like	What it does
Motor	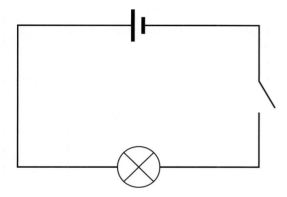 (M)		Turns electricity into movement

△ **Table 13.1** Electrical components

△ **Figure 13.16** Electrical circuit for a simple table lamp

Electrical circuits are usually assembled using soldering. The finished circuit is often housed inside a casing.

13.4 Quality control systems

It is important that quality checks are carried out at all the main stages when making a product. These will normally involve measuring the features changed after each process. If, instead of measuring after each process, you measure only the finished product and you find that one or two measurements are wrong, this can mean you have wasted a lot of time on the other processes.

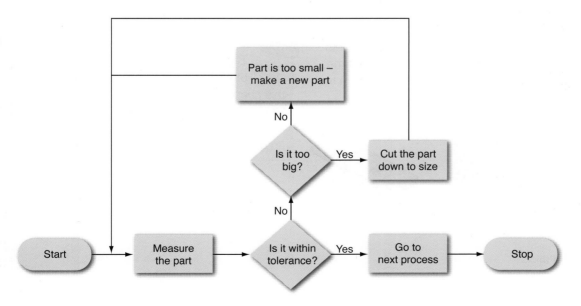

△ **Figure 13.17** Example of a quality check flow chart

In industry, flow charts are often used to provide clear instructions about what to do when checking a part (see Figure 13.17). This helps to turn the instruction into a procedure that all the people making the part must follow.

Jigs and fixtures

Key terms

Jig – a device to hold and position a work piece.

Fixture – a type of jig that is attached to a machine.

Rather than measuring a product after each process to see whether it is the correct size, it is better to design a manufacturing procedure so that it is made correctly in the first place. One way of doing this is to use jigs and fixtures.

A jig is a device made to hold and position a part. It means that the machining operation is carried out in exactly the right place. For example, two holes have to be drilled in 100 pieces of brass. It is important that the separation between the holes is consistent and accurate, so that another part can be slotted into the holes. A jig would be designed to hold the work piece in the same position each time and guide the drill bit so that every hole is in the right place.

If you are making only one part it may not be worth making a jig. However, if you are making lots of parts, a jig can save a significant amount of time and ensure that every part is the same.

A fixture has the same purpose as a jig. The only difference between the two is that the fixture is attached to the base of a machine, whereas a jig can be moved.

Activities

1. Using the internet, for each of the different types of mechanism find an example of a product that uses it. You cannot use the examples given in the book.

2. A company has to manufacture 500 steel plates. Each is 100 mm square and 20 mm thick and has a hole of radius 20 mm in its centre. The hole is at an angle of 45° to the surface, meaning that the metal will have to be held at an angle for drilling. Design a jig or fixture that could be used to manufacture this part using a pillar drill in your school workshop.

Controlled assessment link

The knowledge and understanding of systems and control covered in this chapter, will also be important in your Controlled Assessment. For example, the student's lantern projects in Chapter 2 need an understanding of systems and control.

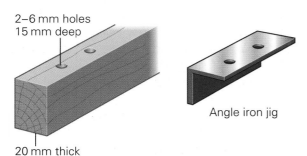

2–6 mm holes
15 mm deep

Angle iron jig

20 mm thick

△ **Figure 13.18** A manufacturing jig for drilling two holes in a piece of wood

Learning objectives

By the end of this chapter you should have developed a knowledge and understanding of:

o how information and communication technology can be used to support research and planning during the development of a design
o how to use computer aided design to generate, develop, model and communicate design ideas
o how to use CAD to present accurate drawings with sizes, using three-dimensional and third-angle orthographic projections, and considering alternative forms and colours when developing ideas
o the latest technologies in designing and making products
o the term CAM, and its applications in your work and industry
o the economic importance and benefits of using CAD/CAM in the production of products
o CAM for manufacturing in quantity
o different machines used in CAM and how they are used
o the advantages/disadvantages of using CAM.

Introduction

Most products are created to meet an identified need. This is normally captured in a design brief. The designer then carries out research and creates ideas for a design solution. Using appropriate information and communication technology (ICT) can greatly reduce the time needed to get from the design brief to the design solution.

This chapter describes how ICT can be used to support the research, recording and presentation of material during the design of a product.

14.1 How developments in ICT have changed product development

Over the past 30 years, developments in ICT have revolutionised how we develop products.

Product development before ICT

Key term

ICT – information and communication technology.

To understand why ICT is used in product development, we need to know how tasks were carried out before ICT existed.

Designers conducted research to identify the needs that a product must meet. They used reference books and libraries. They interviewed customers and examined competitors' products. They carried out basic tests on materials. They would analyse their research themselves, drawing graphs by hand. Much of the information that they gathered was not original or unique. However, often they didn't share it. This was because the research and analysis was very time-consuming. They might be able to use the information they had found to get more work from other customers.

Next, the designer might sketch possible ideas. Once they had developed an idea into a possible design solution, they would prepare presentation drawings by hand, so they could show them to the client or customer. Finally, they would plan the tasks needed to make the product.

For much of this work, the designer often worked on their own. In a large company, they might be helped by a few people in the same office. The development of a new product often took several months. For a complicated product, such as a washing machine or a car, it might even take years.

△ **Figure 14.1** Analysing research without ICT

Product development with ICT

Nowadays, designers share a lot of research information on the internet. They use databases and spreadsheets to sort and analyse it.
They use email to share their findings quickly and easily with other designers. These other designers may be in the same building or could be in another part of the country or even on another continent. They work together to create design ideas using computer software.

Email is also used to share the design ideas with the people who will have to make the product. This lets them use their knowledge of

the manufacturing processes to suggest design improvements that would make the product easier to manufacture. They may also be able to buy the tools and materials that they will need to make the product while the fine details of the design are still being decided. This can speed up the making process significantly. The development of a new product might be completed in just a few weeks.

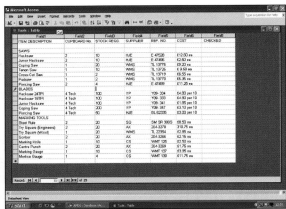

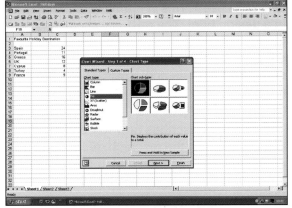

△ **Figure 14.2** Using ICT to analyse research

Activity	How it used to be carried out	How ICT could be used to help carry it out
Researching customer needs	Libraries, reference books, interviewing customers, product analysis	Using information sources on the internet, email or SMS text surveys
Identifying potential customers	Asking people if they use the product, looking at sales records	Using databases listing the customers
Presenting the results of research	Reports typed by hand, with hand-drawn graphs and tables	Word-processed reports, with graphs and tables prepared using spreadsheets such as Excel
Creating drawings	Hand-drawn sketches and drawings	Drawing using computer-aided design software
Testing ideas	Making models and testing them	Creating and testing the actual models using computer-aided design software
Sharing ideas	Internal reports or memos, typed by hand	Email
Sending drawings to manufacturing	Copying the drawing and sending it in the post or delivering it by hand	Email
Finding suppliers for the materials	By visiting companies or trade shows	Using internet search engines
Buying materials	Telephone and post	Email
Planning manufacturing	Engineers prepare separate plans for each product by hand	Computer software prepares plans and also decides what goes on each machine first

△ **Table 14.1** Examples of how ICT is used in industry during product development

14.2 Using ICT in GCSE Resistant Materials projects

In GCSE Resistant Materials, it is essential that you are able to use appropriate ICT. There are several ways that you can provide evidence of this during your controlled assessment:

○ explaining how you found information you used on the internet – for example, this might include listing the search terms that you entered into a search engine

○ listing the web addresses of any sources of information used from the internet
○ recording the results of a questionnaire in a database
○ analysing research using graphs created using a spreadsheet
○ using a word processor to write up findings
○ creating presentation drawings using computer aided design drawing software
○ creating a PowerPoint® presentation showing your design idea and explaining its strengths
○ using a database to create the materials list for the product.

Case study

TSG is a small design company. It works for manufacturing companies. Its business is to create the engineering drawings that are used to communicate sizes when making products.

The designer at TSG receives a design brief from a client company. First, he uses internet search engines to identify similar products. He then looks up technical information (such as sizes) from other internet sources. He uses an Excel spreadsheet to analyse this information. If he needs to justify some of the design features, he might also use Excel to create graphs that he can show to the client.

The designer then sketches some ideas on his computer, using a drawing tablet. He emails them to the client.

The client chooses the idea he likes, and replies by email. The designer then emails the idea to a supplier in India, who will use CAD software to turn the sketch into a working drawing. The Indian supplier works overnight so that the drawings are emailed to TSG for the next morning. TSG then sends them through to the client.

For a simple product, the whole process is completed in less than a week.

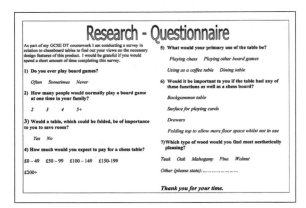

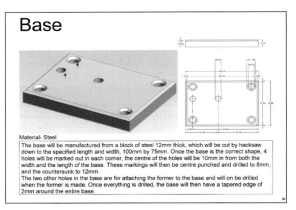

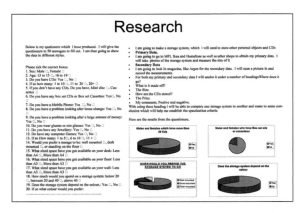

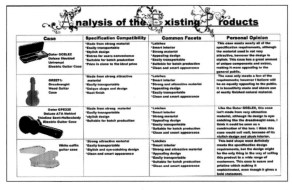

△ **Figure 14.3** Examples of using ICT during GCSE coursework

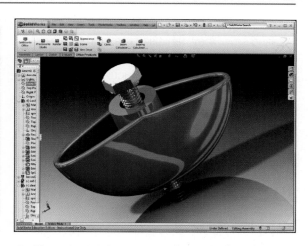

△ **Figure 14.5** A presentation drawing

manufacturers. In the past 20 years or so these programs have been introduced into schools. This has resulted in changes to the type of project produced for examinations.

14.3 What is CAD?

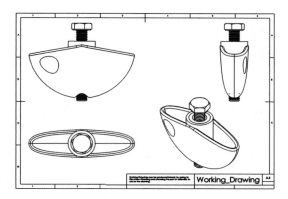

△ **Figure 14.4** A dimensioned working drawing for a part

Computer aided design (CAD), also known as computer aided drafting, is the use of computer software and systems to design and create 2D and/or 3D virtual models of products for the purposes of review or testing prior to manufacture.

There are many different CAD systems available, from freeware which is openly available online to very expensive software as used by specialist

2D CAD

2D CAD produces line drawings that show a profile. Start and end points of straight lines are defined by the x and y coordinates, curved lines are defined by the x and y coordinates of the start and end points and other points in between. These drawings can then be printed out full size for use as a template for cutting out sheet materials

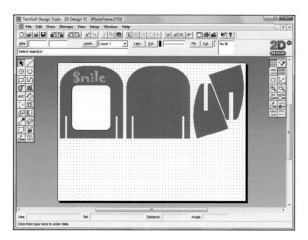

△ **Figure 14.6** A two-dimension drawing page of parts for a photo stand

by hand or a machine such as a band saw or vibrating saw. They can also be exported, using machining software, and used to manufacture the shape using a plotter/cutter machine such as a vinyl cutter or router/milling machine.

When designing with most 2D programs the parts for the project outcomes usually have to be drawn accurately as it can be difficult to change the dimensions once drawn.

3D CAD

3D CAD can be used to design accurately sized complete products as overall design concepts or the individual parts for a design that can be manufactured from those designs. In the program the individual parts can be assembled into the complete artifact and then this assembly can be put to further uses.

Within the 3D CAD drawing every part of the solid is defined by the x, y and z coordinates of each significant point that makes up the drawing. Using a 3D design program allows you to edit the sizes of all parts of the design.

With some software it is possible to set up a relationship between different dimensions so that when you change one dimension others also change in the correct proportion (parametrics). 3D CAD enables changes to a design to be carried out simply and quickly by editing the dimensions and/or the features that created the original design.

Within most 3D CAD programs you can use the 3D drawing of your design to produce other types of drawing. One is an engineering drawing that is generated from the design drawing. This is usually done automatically via a template within the program. You can choose the particular format of the drawing, e.g. third angle orthographic, using a template and all the dimensions are taken through from the original drawing into the engineering drawing.

The other type of drawing that you can produce from your original drawing is a presentation (album) drawing. This gives a more life-like

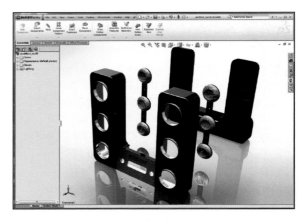

△ **Figure 14.7** A 3D sketch

version of your final idea. It can be rendered in various prospective materials to help in deciding which could be appropriate for its manufacture, and your design can be placed in situ by using an appropriate background created from another drawing or a photograph you have taken of the location for the final product. It produces a more photo-like image of your design.

Controlled assessment link

You will need to use CAD in your Controlled assessment work. The working drawings in Figure 4.25 have been created using CAD.

Key term

Parametrics – defining dimensions for solids as a relationship between one dimension and certain others, e.g. if you set up a relationship between the height of a block and its width such that the Height = 2 x Width then if you dimension the width to be 60 mm the height will automatically be changed to 120 mm. Change the width to 40.5 mm and the height will change to 81 mm.

Advantages of using CAD in designing

Using CAD gives you opportunities to do the following.

○ You can edit your designs at any stage of the process. This allows you to change your design without having to start again. With certain packages you can save different versions within the one file, so reducing the number of files you have to check through to find a particular design. This allows you to 'grow' a branching design, which shows a logical sequence of design development.

○ You can examine your design from all directions and angles so you can do a visual check on your design's appearance. This can help with the modelling stage of the design process.

○ By using different renders you can examine various colour combinations for parts or various materials from which parts of your final design could be manufactured. Rendering can allow a 360° examination of a life-like representation of your design or you can place it within a photo render of the actual situation.

○ Some programs will allow testing of certain aspects of your design, e.g. overall weight of parts (when you define the material), position of the centre of gravity or whether any parts clash when moving a mechanism. Some programs will allow a 'finite element analysis' of an assembly and allows you to test the model by loading it as if it were in use and checking on weaknesses or strengths and allows you to modify your design in order to improve any areas that need changing.

○ You can output your design to a CAM system, which can manufacture exactly what you have designed. You can inspect the manufacturing process with an on-screen simulation before committing to making.

○ Working prototypes can be made using a rapid prototyping machine, which means a full-size or scaled version can be made quickly for inspection before actual manufacture takes place.

○ Files can be emailed from one location to another, enabling designs done in one place to be manufactured at another. Multinational companies make use of this to enable widespread use of designs throughout their plants.

Key term

Prototyping – the manufacture of a single artifact for inspection, evaluating or testing in a real situation. A prototype can be made in the material(s) that the final product is to be made from, or can be made in a different material to test things such as appearance or shaping. For example, you could be designing a brass scoop but rather than make a series of different shaped scoops in brass, which would be expensive and time-consuming, you could evaluate your ideas by making the scoop part of a series of card prototype models before deciding on which is the best way of making the part.

Finite element analysis – a computer model of a material or a design that is stressed and analysed for specific results, allowing you to verify that a proposed design will be able to perform to a client's specifications prior to manufacture. It is a mathematical technique that breaks down a physical structure into substructures called 'finite elements'.

Activities

1. You have been asked to develop a range of key fobs for a family. Taking your own family as a starting point, design a key fob for each member of your family. The fob should include their name and the shape should reflect the person who is to use it.

2. Design a ring box to be manufactured using off-cut blocks. The blocks are 100 mm × 80 mm and are 50 mm thick, and the pieces for a swivelling lid are 20 mm thick. The box base will need a 4 mm diameter hole for the dowel swivel.

3. Design a simple holder for Post-it notes. It should be made up of layers of acrylic that are cemented together to form the unit and use 2 mm diameter rods to ensure each layer is positioned correctly.

4. You wish to display some photographs. Design a photo frame to be made from acrylic. The frame will consist of a front piece which will have a window, to see the photo, a back piece and a supporting piece that has to be used to keep the two other pieces held together.

14.4 What is CAM?

CAM is making parts using a machine that the computer controls. This can be as simple as printing off a full-size drawing of a part to be used as a template, to machines that use powerful lasers or plasma technology, through to sophisticated four- and five-axis machines. Machines can take away material from a blank – often referred to as a subtractive process – or lay down material in layers in a process called additive manufacture.

The CAD data have to be exported in a form that can be understood by the CAM machine. The exported file will have a file extension, which can be a general one such as .stl (stereo-lithography file) or a dedicated file extension for a particular machine. This is a fast-changing area – there are

172

several types of machine that only a few years ago were being used in industry but are now being used in schools.

All machines use the x, y and z values of the part you want to manufacture to refer to any particular position on the part being made. 0,0,0 is the bottom-left corner of your blank or the machine bed when looking down on the bed of the machine. Just as in a graph, the x value is how far to the right you want the cutter centre to be; the y value is how far away you want the tool centre to be from the front edge of the blank; the z value is how high the centre of the end of the tool should be. Whenever using a subtractive process you will often have to tell the machine where the blank is positioned by setting up the 0,0 position in x and y and where the top of the blank is positioned. There are now four- and even some five-axis machines available in schools, which allow even more complex parts to be made.

Cutter machines

The least complex of CAM machines found in schools use a sharp knife tool for cutting thin sheet materials such as card or sticky-back vinyl. The knife blade follows the lines of your design. The knife can be set to score part way through for bend/fold lines when making a card model or completely through to cut out a shape, e.g. vinyl lettering for embellishing a surface. You normally define the depth of cut by using differing colours of line in your drawing. Shallower depths of cut create creases for folds in card.

△ **Figure 14.8** A Roland CAM machine, which can cut vinyl and card, e.g. letters for toy blocks (Figure 14.9)

△ **Figure 14.9** The blocks with vinyl lettering stuck to them

Laser cutters

Key term

Laser – stands for light amplification by stimulated emission of radiation.

Appearing in school workshops over recent times, these machines use a thin beam of tuned light from a laser, which vaporises the material being cut. There needs to be adequate extraction of the resulting fumes from the machine and out into the atmosphere.

The beam has to be tuned to the material being cut – often referred to as the power setting. The other variable in the process is the speed at which the beam passes across the material. Using the correct combination of power and speed will enable you to obtain a high-quality cut to the edge. Get this right and you can obtain a smooth surface that requires the smallest amount of finishing. As the machine laser is used over time it can vary slightly in output and so the relationship between power and speed will need minute adjustment.

The beam of a laser cutter is so small and so accurate that intricate cuts can be made. Lasers can be used to cut a variety of materials, such as MDF (produces a dark-edge surface that has been used as an attractive decorative contrast to the surface colour), timber, paper, card, cloth,

△ **Figure 14.10** Laser CAM A2

laminates, ceramics or circuit boards. As there is no contact with a tool you seldom need to fasten down the material being processed and so have one less health and safety consideration, although some materials have been known to burn when the wrong settings have been input and so flammable materials need attention – the brown edge on MDF is evidence of the heat generated at the point of the cut.

The machine burns through the material using several passes that cut progressively deeper and so the machine can be used for engraving into a surface. Manufacturers make special engraving laminates with layers of contrasting colours of material, of which the top layer can be removed to enable signs and so on to be manufactured.

The major advantage of using a laser cutter is the speed of set-up, speed of manufacture and the minimal amount of finishing usually required before assembly. As the beam is so small, parts can be arranged for cutting closer together than when using machines that use a tool to cut out the material. This means you can produce less waste material when manufacturing, especially if manufacturing in quantity. There is still a need for a tool offset even though the beam is thin – not using an offset will result in the part being microscopically smaller than the intended design. Most machines will automatically calculate the amount and position of the offset.

Plasma cutters

Plasma is the fourth state of matter. We all are familiar with the first three: solid, liquid and gas. A plasma cutter works by sending an electric arc through a gas that is being compressed by forcing it through a nozzle. This gas can be air, nitrogen, argon, oxygen, etc. The metal to be cut completes the electrical circuit so the arc runs from the electrode inside the nozzle by way of the gas to the surface of the metal. Electricity flowing through the compressed gas converts the gas into the state called plasma and this creates a very thin, very high-temperature arc, which becomes a fine flame that cuts through the metal.

The machine cuts any sheet metal and works just as any other CNC machine – controlled by a computer. Your design is converted into data, which is fed to the machine. The torch head travels at around 2m per minute. The major advantage of a plasma cutter is that it works so fast and produces very smooth cut edges, meaning minimal finishing is needed.

Water and abrasive jet cutters

Abrasive jet and water-only jet cutters use high-pressure water, usually between 30,000 and 60,000 psi (pounds per square inch) to create an extremely concentrated jet to cut through materials. A water cutter, without abrasive, pressurises a thin stream of pure water to cut through materials such as foam, rubber, plastic, cloth or wood.

An abrasive jet cutter mixes an abrasive stone called a garnet, which is in fine powder form, into a pressurised water stream to cut harder materials. Examples are stainless steel, titanium, glass, ceramic tile, marble and granite.

One advantage of a water jet metal-cutting machine is that it will produce very little heat at the point of cut. This means there will be no heat-affected zone (HAZ) and so in most cases further heat treatment will not be required as is often the case with a plasma cutter. Water

jet machining is also a 'cold cut' process and therefore is safe for cutting flammable materials such as plastic and polymers.

Milling/routing machines

These machines control cutting tools called an end mill. This tool has spiral cutting flutes up the side of the tool and two cutting surfaces across the radius of the end of the tool. This gives a flat-bottomed, vertical walled cut. Another tool that can be used is a ball-end mill. This tool is similar to the end mill, with cutting flutes down the sides, but has a hemispherical cutting end.

If you used the edge of the material (part line) to drive the manufacturing sequence, the middle of the tool would follow the lines on your design and the tool would cut into the piece you require. If you used the drawn line to define the tool pathway, the finished part would be smaller by twice the radius of the tool as the inside half of the tool would be cutting into the part required (or the outside of the tool when cutting an internal hole). To overcome this problem you have to use a tool offset. Most programs allow you to generate tool offset lines automatically in the drawing stage and define the z-value of the line by using different colours for different depths of cut. In Figure 14.12 the black line is the part line and the red line shows the centre line for the cutter to follow.

△ **Figure 14.11** CNC milling machine

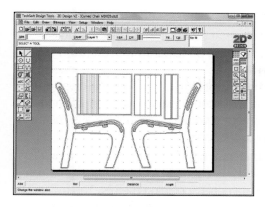

△ **Figure 14.12** Drawing ready for use in manufacture

The z-value is the depth of the cut needed for that particular line. Using this process you can cut out any that made up of a series of lines to be cut at different depths. The machine will generate the shallowest cuts first and then work through the depths to the deepest cut. This linear cutting is a much quicker process than cutting a solid, which has constantly changing x, y and z values defining the solid.

When creating a solid with constantly varying z depth, such as a mould for a face mask, you need to use a different machining strategy. You instruct the machine to cut a pathway with a constantly changing z value. The first decision you must make is whether to cut out your part using a tool pathway that travels, or rasters, in either an x-direction or y-direction, though sometimes you may ask it to travel first in one direction and then in the other. However, this will double the time taken to manufacture.

As the tool travels in a straight line across the part the tip will be moved up and down so the

tool produces the top surface of the part. When it comes to the end of its travel in, say, the x-direction, it will move across slightly in y before travelling back in the reverse x-direction. This is known as the stepover and is usually defined as a percentage of the tool diameter.

The smaller the stepover, the larger the number of passes needed to cover the whole surface of the part. This results in the making process being much longer and is a dilemma as, the larger the stepover, the rougher the top surface will be as you would normally be using a round-nosed tool and each pass will leave a small ridge between passes. Manufacturing using this strategy often takes so long that machines are left running overnight. This is known as 'lights-out machining'.

There are usually two machining sequences – roughing and finishing. Roughing is the process that removes most of the waste. Some simpler products do not need a roughing pass and the finishing pass can be the only pass.

○ Roughing usually uses a larger-diameter tool and the stepover is usually a larger percentage of the tool diameter.

○ Finishing is usually done with a smaller-diameter tool and the stepover is usually set as small as 10–15 per cent or even smaller.

Planning this strategy is so complex that it is mostly done by using a computer program, often referred to as a 'wizard'. The program allows the maker to define the machining data using a series of screens which asks them to make decisions over steps in the process. The program then calculates the tool pathway for each stage of manufacture and does in minutes what previously took skilled workers many hours. The output is usually seen on-screen as a graphic simulation of the process. The instructions to the machine are in a stream of a coded steps, which the machine interprets as the tool movement. Skilled workers can still edit this program output and make slight changes to the manufactured outcome.

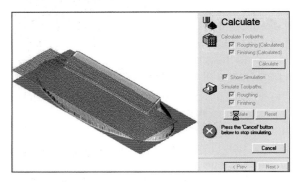

△ **Figure 14.13** Screenshot of a wizard starting to simulate first cut of machine as set up using previous screens

In schools these are usually three-axis machines, but there are some four-axis machines used in schools where the first three are the same as a three-axis machine and the fourth axis is rotation, which enables more complex surfaces to be produced.

School machines are usually used for one-off manufacture, but if you are making several identical parts you may design and make a holding jig that blanks can be fastened into quickly and the parts made without having to set up the machine each time. These machines often have a rotating turret, which allows the use of several different tools to carry out different cuts without stopping the machine and manually changing the tools.

One difference between a miller and a router is that a miller is capable of cutting through much harder materials, including metals. The miller spindle speed is slower and it is fitted with a higher-powered motor, which allows it to cut harder materials than a router without any tool deflection – meaning a smoother, more accurate cut. The miller is capable of machining a wide range of resistant materials, but it does so at a slower speed. The router traverses at much higher speeds and the bed of a router is usually much larger than a milling machine, enabling larger parts to be manufactured.

> ## Key term
> **Fixture/holding jig** – a holding device that you can fix to the bed of a CNC machine and use it to position and secure blanks for the making process. This enables you to manufacture a single prototype and also allows you to move to batch production without the need to reset the tool position to the blank each time as the blank is always held in the same position as the first blank.

CNC lathes

> ## Key term
> **CNC** – computer numerically controlled. This describes the use of digital language to run a machine. Digital language is made up of a series of 0s and 1s, which are interpreted by the machine in a step-by-step process.

CNC lathes were one of the first CAM machines used in schools but are now being replaced in some cases by four- and five-axis machines. These machines revolve while the tool follows a drawn profile. Initially the profile had to be drawn on graph paper and the coordinates of each part of the profile worked out and input into the machining data as a series of G-codes or M-codes, giving tool position, machine speed and travel speed, and direction.

However, this was time consuming – it often took over an hour to write the codes to get the machine parameters set up and get the tool into its position to make the first cut – so led to the creation of the machining wizard programs we use today. They are useful for cutting external and internal screw threads, and for a series of identical drawer knobs or similar turned items.

Older machines are being supplemented by more versatile machining centres, which can carry out a variety of machining processes on a part using four or more axes machining.

Rapid prototyping machines

Often referred to as 3D printers, rapid prototyping (RP) machines build up a solid by making very thin layers of the product. The machine has a dedicated program that takes your design and slices it into a series of layers and then outputs these layers to the machine. These slices are then piled on top of each other to make the solid. The thickness of each layer determines the quality of the outcome: the thicker the layer, the rougher the model surface.

The simplest RP machine cuts series of paper or vinyl layers, which have reference holes in them to allow easy assembly. These are then stuck together to create the solid. This is known as laminated object modelling (LOM). There are more sophisticated machines that work in a variety of materials. Most, if not all, make the solid you have designed and some also make a softer, crumblier material that is used to

△ **Figure 14.14** A CNC training lathe

△ **Figure 14.15** A 3D rapid prototyping machine

support the solid where there is a space or void underneath it as the machine goes up through the layers.

Stereo lithography machines use a bath of epoxy resin liquid, which is fused into a solid layer where two or more lasers cross. These layers are built up on top of each other to make the designed solid either by the bed dropping down by the thickness of each layer or by the laser crossing point moving up by the same distance.

Selective laser sintering (SLS) is where a powder is laid down in microscopic layers one layer at a time. Each layer is fused by a laser after it is deposited. As each layer is laid down, the bed moves down by the layer thickness and the next layer is laid down. The powder can be plastic, metal, ceramic or a combination of these. This enables a realistically strong prototype to be made and this can be used for evaluation in a working environment.

Fused deposition modelling machines are a little like a computer-controlled hot melt glue gun, where a reel of small-diameter material such as wax or polymer like ABS is extruded through a heated nozzle to create the prototype. There is a second nozzle that extrudes a softer material used to build support pegs. As each layer is laid down, the bed moves down by the layer thickness and the next layer is laid down. Support materials can then be crushed off by hand and the surfaces smoothed down using wet and dry paper.

Why use CAM?

A CAM file is capable of being stored electronically, so it can be taken from one machine to another on a storage device such as a pen drive. A file can also be emailed from one location to anywhere in the world. This has led to the globalisation of industrial manufacturing. Parts can be made in different locations and assembled in another. Identical products can be manufactured in a variety of locations.

CAM is more accurate than hand manufacturing and can be repeated to a constant quality. It is often much quicker and can be done 24 hours a day, enabling greater productivity from the machines as they never need to take a break except for maintenance and can be used with little supervision.

CAM is safer than hand manufacturing when harmful chemicals or materials are being used in the process. In industry, as in schools, however, very few products can be entirely made using

100 per cent CAM – most are made using a combination of CAM and hand processes. Striking a balance between CAM and hand processes is a big dilemma in manufacturing – CAM machines mean vast investment but are faster; skilled workers need costly training whichever system is used; less skilled and therefore cheaper, workers can supervise CAM production, etc.

The availability of more and more powerful computer systems has enabled companies to integrate the whole process of design, analysis, production, purchasing, inventory control, manufacturing and distribution to be run by a single computer system (Computer integrated manufacture – CIM), though individual computers will run individual processes or machines within the total system. A part may be machined in several different computer-controlled machines and computer-controlled robots used to transport the part from one to another and set them up automatically and accurately. Sensors are connected to computers to check out accurate positioning and the progress of parts around the system.

 ## Key term

CIM (computer integrated manufacture) – where the whole production process is controlled by computers.

Advantages of CAM

CAM enables:

- continuous and faster production
- much improved consistency in product outcome quality
- cheaper production because the process is less labour intensive
- machines to be quickly reset to manufacture a different product
- files to be sent worldwide to enable the electronic exchange of information within a company; they can also be worked on at

home or anywhere in school, or sent to an external manufacturing site such as an FE college or university lab, where you can have access to a more sophisticated machine than in school.

Disadvantages of CAM

o Data can be lost if not stored correctly or a backup has not been made.

o The machines require a significant investment in purchase or lease.
o In industry, the machine operatives need costly training for each new machine or software change.
o These machines need fewer operatives than manual machines and so require a reduced workforce, resulting in raised unemployment.

Activities

In the CAD section above you had the chance to design several projects. Here we will use these designs to prepare for manufacturing the articles. The first problems are done in more detail than the later designs – use your experience with the first two to guide you when answering the later ones.

1. You have designs for your key fobs. Assemble all the designs for your family on one drawing page ready for cutting them out in one machining run.

   o Decide on one tool diameter for cutting out the shape and engraving the letters.
   o Create the machining pathways by setting the tool offsets (a) for the shape and (b) for the engraving. (Remember these two will be cut to different depths and will need more than one pass to cut the whole depth – if making them from 4 mm material, set the maximum depth of cut to 2 mm.)
   o Set up the spindle speed for your chosen tool.
   o Set up the travel speed for the tool.
   o Simulate the machining process to check it out.
   o Save the machining data for the appropriate machine.

2. You have designed a ring box. Use the plan view of the shape to prepare for cutting out the block.

   o Choose an appropriate-sized tool and create a tool offset for the outside shape.
   o Create a tool offset for the inside shape using a different colour line as this cut will not be as deep.
   o Create more offsets from this line until you reach the centre of the space.
   o Create an offset for the dowel hole.
   o Set up the spindle speed for your chosen tool.
   o Set up the travel speed for the tool.
   o Simulate the machining process to check it out.
   o Save the machining data for the appropriate machine.

3. You have designed a simple holder for Post-it notes. Assemble all the layers side by side so as to take up as small a space as possible. Choose an appropriate-sized tool for machining out your design. Set up the machining parameters for your tool and create the machining data for your chosen machine.

4. You have designed a photo frame to be made from acrylic. Assemble the parts on one drawing – taking up as small a space as possible. Choose an appropriate-sized tool for machining out your design. Set up the machining parameters for your tool and create the machining data for your chosen machine.

Key term

Machining parameters – the data you input into the machining program in order to set up the machine for optimum performance. When using Techsoft2D it can be done using the Pens/Tools button in Plotting Devices. Usually involves giving a line colour, a specific total depth of cut, a tool diameter, a travel speed, a spindle speed and a maximum depth of cut per pass.

14.5 When can CAD and CAM contribute to my Controlled Assessment task?

Computers can help with word processing for creating and editing text as well as using databases or the internet for research. Digital images can be used in collecting research or photographing models. These images of models can then be used for drawing and rendering your development ideas.

When can you use CAD during the design process?

There are several strategies you could adopt.

1. When you start drawing your design ideas you may begin to use CAD. At this stage you need to be 'thinking on paper' so when choosing to use CAD you should be capable of drawing quickly to illustrate your design thinking, using your chosen software. If you would be quicker

using hand sketching then perhaps CAD is not appropriate for you at this stage.

2. When you have chosen one or two 'best ideas' for presentation to a client, if you have one, then preparing CAD drawings of these design concepts may be the time to start using CAD.

3. When beginning the development stage of designing you may find it appropriate to start using CAD. Drawing the individual parts of the overall product will enable you to use a basic design of each component part to suggest alternative constructions and examine different ways of making the overall project.

4. You could use CAD in the development stage to draw simple models with different stylings of an overall design. These could be manufactured as scale models to be evaluated and to contribute to design development.

5. Having completed the development of your chosen idea using hand graphics, you could use CAD to produce drawings of individual parts based on your final idea. In 2D CAD these would be full-size, accurate drawings of individual parts, which could be printed out as working drawings or templates from which parts could be cut by hand or exported as a file that your CAM machine can understand to enable manufacturing to take place. In 3D CAD individual parts can then be assembled into an assembly drawing that can be used to produce a fully dimensioned orthographic working drawing using the software. Individual drawings can then be exported in a form that your CAM machine is capable of understanding and using to make those parts.

6. When you have a final assembly drawing of your design you can then use it to produce an engineering drawing and dimension it to be used as a working drawing. Parts of this drawing can also be used to drive the manufacturing stage.

7. You can also use your final assembly drawing to produce an album drawing, which can be rendered and used as a presentation drawing and could be given to your client or end user for evaluation prior to manufacturing.

Key term

CAD CAM – the integrated process of designing and making an artifact or parts for an artifact using a computer and appropriate software.

Exam tips

The advantage of using CAD is the accuracy that you can achieve. Whatever dimensions you input into the drawing will be reproduced accurately when the drawing is used in manufacturing. CAD drawings enable you to manufacture the same part over and over again with accuracy. This is called repetition – you can repeatedly manufacture identical parts by using CAD and CAM – which is good for batch production. You can usually produce parts more quickly by using CAM than by hand and parts usually need less finishing, depending on the type of machine used.

CAM can be used in the modelling stages of development by quickly creating models that can be evaluated and their images used for sketching development ideas on top of these images. CAM can be used to make parts for your final ideas where appropriate.

Using CAD and CAM can allow you to tackle a more complex Design and Make task than one using just hand skills. It can speed up the completion of your task, leaving you time for more detailed testing of the outcome, and possibly time for further modification of the idea and manufacturing of improved parts for

an improved outcome. You could also have time to make different outcomes from your ideas and carry out comparative evaluations of these.

One thing you should do as part of your folder is show how you used your CAD drawings to run the CAM machines. If you are using a simpler program where lines are cut to differing depths, you need to show how you used the program to define the depth of cut each pass, number of passes, maximum cutter depth for each line, spindle speed and travel speed.

If you are using a wizard program to drive your CAM machine you should show how you used each page of the wizard to define the process. Both these can be shown by using screenshots, by using either the print screen key or a screen capture program. These images, together with explanatory notes, will show that you understand exactly how to convert your drawings into the parts you need.

You do not have to use CAD or CAM within your Controlled Assessment task – just decide if and when using them is appropriate.

chapter 15
Industrial practices

>
> ### Learning objectives
> By the end of this chapter you should have developed a knowledge and understanding of:
> - types of manufacturing system, including one-off, batch and high-volume
> - how the quantity of products being made and the choice of the manufacturing system affect the cost of making the product
> - how the roles of the client, designer and manufacturer in the development of products vary between different manufacturing systems.

Introduction

The number of parts that need to be made has a major effect on the types of machine that are used to make them. It also affects how these machines are organised, and the roles of the people involved in the design and manufacture of the product.

This chapter describes three common categories of production. It explains how these categories affect the approach to the making of a product, in terms of both the manufacturing system used and the activities of the people involved.

15.1 Scale of production

The scale of production refers to the number of parts to be made. It is often classified into three types:

- one-off
- batch
- high-volume.

> ### Key terms
> **Job production** – another name for one-off production.
>
> **Batch production** – manufacturing a specified quantity of the same product.
>
> **Mass production** – a type of high-volume production.

One-off production

One-off production is sometimes called job production. It refers to making one or a very small number of products. The types of products range from spectacle lenses, designer jewellery and custom-designed furniture, to satellites and special parts needed to repair large machines. Most GCSE Resistant Materials controlled assessment project work is carried out as one-off production.

△ **Figure 15.1** Example of a one-off product – a satellite

Batch production

If a manufacturing company were making 100 coffee tables, it wouldn't make them one at a time, finishing each one before starting the next. It would make 100 table tops, then 400 legs, then assemble the tables.

Batch production involves making a specified quantity of the same product. The size of the batch might range from fewer than ten to a few thousand, depending upon the type of product. The batch might be repeated at a later date if it is needed again.

Examples of products made in batches include parts for Formula 1 cars, musical instruments and most household furniture.

△ **Figure 15.2** Example of a batch-produced product – a trumpet

High-volume production

High-volume production is where large quantities of one type of product are made. The quantities involved might range from a few hundred to tens of thousands of products per day, depending upon the type of product. The products are often identical. Many of the items that we use every day are produced in high volumes. They include nuts and bolts, mobile phones, cars and bars of chocolate.

△ **Figure 15.3** Example of a product produced in high volumes – a television

15.2 **Manufacturing systems**

Key term

Manufacturing system – a system in which machines are used for production, and how they are organised.

What we do to material to make something is called a process. The processes used to make a product are normally determined by the design of the product. For example, material might need to be removed or shaped, or a finish might need to be applied.

However, often there are several different tools or machines that could be used to carry out or support these processes. Further, these can be organised for use in a number of ways. The combination of which machines to use and the method of organising them is known as the manufacturing system.

The scale of production has a significant effect on which manufacturing system is chosen to make a product.

One-off production

One-off production is often carried out using machines that are very flexible in terms of how they are used. This means they can be used to make lots of different types of products.

The machines used are often manually controlled – the operator controls how the tool in the machine moves. Where accuracy is important, computer-controlled machines might be used. These can often carry out machining processes faster than manually controlled machines. However, because of the time it takes to program the computer-controlled machines, in total they may need more labour time than a manually controlled machine.

In a workshop that carries out one-off production, the machines may often be grouped together by the process that they carry out. For example, all the lathes might be in one area and the milling machines in a different area. The reason for this is that the machines are operated by highly skilled workers. These workers sometimes specialise in an individual process, such as turning, milling or grinding. However, depending upon how much skill the unique product needs, sometimes the same worker might carry out all the processes needed to make the product.

The machines will normally be set up to make the one-off job by the operator. This means that he will put the tools needed to make the product onto the machine, enter the machine settings and measure them so that they are correct. The operator will then run the machine. As a result of the set-up time and the manual control by the operator, one-off production often uses a lot of labour time.

Batch production

In batch production, once a machine has been set up it will be used to make all of the products in the batch. It is often carried out using computer-controlled machines. If more than one

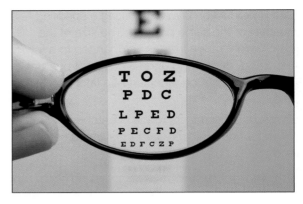

△ **Figure 15.4** Spectacle lenses have to be made to fit the unique requirements of the wearer's eyes

process is needed, it is likely that they will be carried out by different skilled operators.

Templates and jigs are often used to mark up and position the parts in batch production. They reduce the set-up time and help to ensure that machining is always carried out in the same place. These are often made by specialist toolmakers. They can be quite expensive,

---

Case study

One-off production of gears

David Brown Engineering is one of the world's leading manufacturers of specialist gears.

One part of its business is to supply large gears for use in industrial machines. The machines themselves are often one-offs, and each gear is unique. A single gear can weigh more than 100 tons!

The gear has to be made to the exact size the customer needs. This requires great skill, using a wide range of manufacturing processes. Every process is set up and operated by a highly skilled worker. More than 20 workers might be involved in the production of each gear.

△ **Figure 15.5** A one-off gear

but with batch production the cost is divided between all the parts in the batch.

If a lot of similar products are being made, the machines might be arranged in a manufacturing cell. This means that all of the machines needed to make the product will be positioned close to each other. This saves time moving the batch of products between different machines in the workshop.

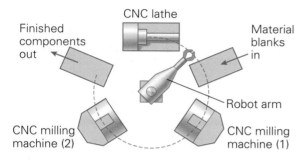

△ **Figure 15.6** A manufacturing cell: the parts are moved between the processes by a robot arm

Key term

Cellular manufacture – a manufacturing system where the different machines needed to make a product are located with each other.

High-volume production

Key term

Production line – a manufacturing system where a group of machines is dedicated to the complete manufacture of a product, normally in large quantities.

High-volume production is sometimes called mass production. Due to the large quantity of products being made, it is often carried out on dedicated machines. This means that a machine is used only to make that product. The machines will probably use fixtures to position the parts.

 ## Case study

Batch production of musical instruments

Calder & Sons manufactures electric guitars. The guitars are normally made in batches of 10–20. The company has more than 100 design variations, which it supplies to order.

A template is used to mark out the shape of the guitar body on the wood for that batch. This is then cut out by hand using a bandsaw. A second worker then uses a computer-controlled machine to remove material to allow the electrical components to be installed. The machine uses a jig to position the body to make sure that everything is in the right place.

The components and other parts are assembled by a third worker. A finish is applied in a spray booth by a fourth worker and, finally, each guitar is tested by the company's resident musician.

△ **Figure 15.7** A batch of guitars

These are similar to jigs, but permanently attached to the bed of the machine.

The machines will normally be computer controlled. Many may also have automation or robot arms to load and unload the parts into them.

The machines will often be organised in a production line. This is where the processes used to make a product are put in order, so that they can carry out all of the steps on the production plan in sequence. Sometimes a conveyor belt will run the length of the production line, moving the product between the different processes or activities that need to be carried out.

△ **Figure 15.8** A car production line

Selecting the manufacturing system

Making products is normally about making money. The choice of which manufacturing system to use is normally based on how much it will cost to make the product. Calculating this cost can be quite tricky. There are lots of different things that will add to it. These are normally split into two types of cost: fixed and variable.

Fixed costs

Fixed costs are things that stay the same no matter how many products you decide to make. They include the cost of the building, and any machines, tools, jigs and fixtures bought to make that product.

In the case of one-off and batch production, normally the fixed costs do not include the full cost

of the machines used to make the product. This is because these machines will be used to make lots of different products over their life. Hence the fixed cost includes only a part of the costs of the machines. However, it will include the full cost of any jigs and templates made for that product.

In high-volume production, the machines will be used to make only that product. Hence the full cost of the machine is counted.

Variable costs

Variable costs are things where, the more products you need to make, the more you will have to spend. They include the materials needed and the cost of the labour to make the product. For example, to make two products you will need twice as much material as to make one product.

Total cost and cost per part

The total cost of production is the sum of the fixed and variable costs. The actual cost per part is the total cost divided by the number of parts being made.

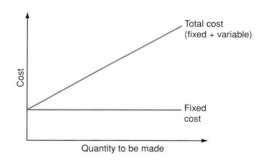

△ **Figure 15.9** Total cost of production

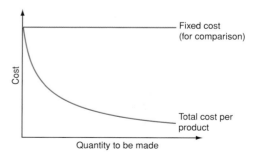

△ **Figure 15.10** Cost per product

How costs vary between manufacturing systems

In general, one-off production has low fixed costs but high variable costs. This is because a lot of skilled labour time is used to make the product. This manufacturing system normally gives the highest cost per product made.

In batch production, jigs and fixtures have to be made and the machines used are often computer

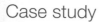 Case study

A car engine consists of hundreds of component parts. During the initial development of a new car engine, one-off parts are supplied so that the designers can test ideas. Once they are happy with the initial design, a batch of cars is made to check the performance and make small improvements. Finally, when the car goes into full production, the product will be produced in high volumes. For cars, this can be more than 10,000 products per day, with production continuing for five or more years.

Table 15.1 shows how the cost of one of the parts used varies with the number of products being made and the manufacturing system used.

One-off production to test ideas

Number of parts made	Contribution to fixed cost (£)	Variable cost per part (£)	Total cost (£)	Cost per part (£)
1	2,000	300	2,300	2,300

Batch production to check the performance

Number of parts made	Contribution to fixed cost (£)	Variable cost per part (£)	Total cost (£)	Cost per part (£)
10	6,500	50	7,000	700.00
100	6,500	50	11,500	115.00
1,000	6,500	50	56,500	56.50
10,000	6,500	50	506,500	50.65

High-volume production

Number of parts made	Fixed cost (£)	Variable cost per part (£)	Total cost (£)	Cost per part (£)
10,000	300,000	20	500,000	50.00
100,000	300,000	20	2,300,000	23.00
500,000	300,000	20	10,300,000	20.60
1,000,000	300,000	20	20,300,000	20.30

△ **Table 15.1** Manufacturing costs for different scales of production

controlled. This results in slightly higher fixed costs than one-off production. However, these help to reduce the labour cost in the variable cost.

In high-volume manufacture, the machines are dedicated to the product they are making. They often use conveyor belts and robots to move products between machines. This results in very high fixed costs. However, there is normally very little labour time needed – machines do most of the work, so the variable costs are low. As the fixed cost can be divided between so many products, this can result in the lowest overall cost to make the product.

15.3 **Working within a manufacturing system**

Several roles can be identified during the process of developing a product. These include the client, the designer, the people who make the product, and the user. How these roles work with each

other is often strongly influenced by the scale of production.

One-off production

In one-off production, a unique product is being made. Often, the client is the same person as the user. They provide a design brief for the product they want. For products such as designer furniture or jewellery, the person who receives the brief might design the product and then make it themselves.

This means that the person who designs and makes the product can have a clear understanding of what the person who is paying for the product wants.

Batch production

In batch production, sometimes the client is also the user of the product. However, sometimes the client is intending to sell the product to the users.

Case study

One-off production of furniture

Colin James is a skilled joiner. His business is making designer furniture for individual customers. This ranges from coffee tables to chairs to kitchen cabinets and wardrobes. He works in his own workshop, with one assistant. The workshop includes a wide range of general woodworking equipment.

When a customer calls Colin, he goes to visit them. They tell him what they want and he takes any measurements that are needed. For example, many customers want cabinets or wardrobes to fit in a specific space in their house. He sketches out some ideas and the customer chooses what they would like.

Colin then calculates the sizes of the wood he needs. After buying it, he makes the piece

of furniture in his workshop. He uses all of the different machines himself. Finally, he delivers it to the customer and gives them his bill.

△ **Figure 15.11** A piece of custom-made wooden furniture

Normally, the client will provide the design brief to a designer. The designer will provide the design to the people who will make the product. They will provide the product to the client. Normally the designer and the people who will make the product are employed by the same manufacturing company.

High-volume production

In high-volume production, the client normally intends to sell the product. There may be a team of specialist designers and engineers responsible for developing the product. Manufacturing will be carried out in a factory. This might be near to the design team, or it could even be in a different country. The finished products will often be sent directly to the shops or to the users.

Activities

1. Using the internet, identify three examples for each scale of production. You cannot use the examples given in this chapter.

2. Carry out a product analysis of a piece of flat-pack furniture. For each part used in the furniture, identify the scale of production that was used to make it.

Controlled assessment link

As part of your Controlled Assessment work it will be helpful to have an understanding of industrial practices and how they differ from the practices you will use at school.

chapter 16
Controlled assessment

Your AQA GCSE in Resistant Materials will be assessed in two parts:

1. A two-hour written examination. This is worth 40 per cent of your overall GCSE.

2. A Controlled Assessment, which will take about 45 hours. This is worth 60 per cent of your GCSE.

To achieve the best result, you need to do the best you can in both parts of the assessment. This chapter will look at the Controlled Assessment, in which you carry out a Design and Make activity.

The Controlled Assessment is a Design and Make project. It is a timed piece of work that is carried out in class, in the presence of your teacher. You will have about 45 hours to complete it, which is often spread over many weeks in class.

The starting point for your Controlled Assessment will be a design brief, set by the examination board. You will use this to produce a design folder of approximately 20 A3 pages, along with a manufactured outcome. The folder will normally contain pictures of your finished product, to provide evidence of the standard of your work. It is important to understand that it is not the quantity of the work that will earn the marks, but the level of detail and quality it includes.

The sheets in the design folder should follow a design process. Ideally the emphasis and volume of work of each part of the folder should relate to the marks available in the assessment.

During the 45 hours, your teacher is not able to give you individual, specific advice on how to address the marking criteria or how to improve your work. However, your class might be given general advice and feedback. Outside of the allotted time, you may have teaching and learning as usual. This might be relevant to the part of the Controlled Assessment you are completing. It will be your job to apply this and your prior learning into your GCSE work.

You and your teacher must sign a Candidate Record Form confirming that your work is your own original work. Your work will be assessed by your teacher(s). The marks will be sent to the examination board and moderated to AQA standards.

In summary, you will:

o have about 45 hours to complete a design and make project, based on a design brief set by the exam board.

o produce a design folder of about 20 pages of A3 or equivalent.

o produce a manufactured outcome. Photographic evidence will be required.

16.1 The design process and the Controlled Assessment criteria

A design process is a series of steps that are carried out to develop a product. These steps might be carried out one after the other as a logical sequence, or they might be carried out as a continuous loop. Sometimes as you proceed through the process, you might also find things out which mean that you have to go back to previous steps.

The exam board awards marks for certain activities carried out within the design process. This means that your design folder needs to contain good evidence of your work in each of these areas. The marks available are shown in Table 16.1.

A good project will have detail and work in each of these areas. Each of the above sections has an assessment statement attached to it. This describes what the work will look like or the detail that it will include to achieve certain ranges of marks. The mark that will be awarded to your

Assessment criteria	Maximum mark	Percentage
Investigating the design context	8	9%
Development of the design proposal, including modelling	32	34%
Making	32	34%
Testing and evaluation	12	14%
Communication	8	9%
Total	**90**	**100%**

△ **Table 16.1** Marks available for Controlled Assessment

work will depend upon how well it 'fits' against the assessment statement.

The brief

The brief is normally the starting point for the design process. It is a short statement of the problem to be solved. It may also give you an outline of some other factors that are considered for your project.

AQA provide a list of design briefs. Your teacher might select which ones would be the most appropriate for you and your class based upon facilities available.

From the brief you can identify what you need to know to design your product, and use this to plan the research that you will use to find out this information.

16.2 Investigating the design context

This involves identifying what you need to know to be able to design a solution to the design problem. The assessment statements for investigating the design context are shown in Table 16.2.

Criterion 1 mark band	Investigating the design context
7–8	<ul><li>Discrimination shown when selecting and acquiring relevant research that will promote originality in designing</li><li>Excellent understanding and analysis of the design context</li><li>Detailed analysis of relevant existing products or systems undertaken related to design intentions</li><li>Comprehensive analysis of relevant and focused research undertaken</li><li>Clear and specific design criteria identified, reflecting the analysis undertaken</li><li>Target market identified and the intended consumer/user profiled</li></ul>

△ **Table 16.2** Investigating the design context   *Contd*

Criterion 1 mark band	Investigating the design context
5–6	o Good understanding and analysis of the design context o Good analysis of relevant products or systems undertaken o Good analysis of relevant research and context o Design criteria which reflects the analysis undertaken o Target market for product has been identified
3–4	o Basic understanding and analysis of the design context o Some analysis of related products or systems undertaken o Made a superficial analysis of most of the research material and the context o Design criteria reflects most of the analysis undertaken o Some consideration has been taken of the likely consumer/user
0–2	o Limited understanding or analysis of design context o Minimal analysis of other products or systems undertaken o Provided little evidence of research and analysis of context o Design criteria is very general and lacking in any detail o Limited understanding of the target market/user evident

△ **Table 16.2** Investigating the design context

To achieve a mark in the highest band of this criterion you could consider including the following in your work:

o A profile of the people who will use the product that you are designing.
o Evidence of a wide range of research strategies. These might include, as a starting point, the following:
  o Evaluating and taking apart existing products
  o User surveys
  o Investigations into different materials that could be used
  o Investigations into different manufacturing processes that could be used
o Graphs and tables showing the results of the research and explaining what these results mean for your design.
o A list of the important design criteria for your product.

The aim of research is to find information that will help you to design an effective product. Potentially, this might appear to be a massive task. However, bear in mind that the whole project should come to 20 pages of A3. If we were to apply a formulae of percentage of marks awarded to sheets used, this whole section would need to be completed in two pages.

That said, your research will almost certainly be more than two sides. This is because it forms the foundation for your Controlled Assessment. If you know all the requirements that your product must meet, it will be much easier to design and you will use your time more effectively. This also helps to stop problems later on. For example, imagine that you have designed and made a child's toy. If you were to discover when evaluating your finished product that its size was too small and parts created a choking risk, or that the finish used could be poisonous, then you might have to spend a lot of time going back and redesigning it, re-planning production and making the new design. Time spent doing research can almost be seen as an insurance policy against this happening!

Your research should be succinct, focused and relevant to the product that you will be designing. For example, if your analysis of the design brief and initial research concludes that the product should be made from plastic, there is no point wasting time investigating what processes could be used to make it from metal.

One particularly important part of research is product analysis. This involves looking at, and taking apart, products made by other manufacturers. It allows you to identify the good features of their designs, and areas where they can be improved. In effect, it saves you some time by using the results of their research. Most often you will look at similar products, but you might look at unrelated products that have features that are relevant to you. For example, if you were designing a box with a lid, you might also investigate different ways of attaching the lid, by looking at devices used to attach cupboard doors, car doors, supermarket doors etc.

It can often help to sketch interesting features of the product you are analysing, and add labels to show the examiner why you think that feature is relevant to your design. It can also help to use an acronym like ACCESS FM to help you remember all the areas that you need to look at.

Knowledge link
For more information on ACCESS FM, refer to Chapter 2.

Your research will generate data. To make sure that your time is used effectively, you need to analyse this data and show how it may affect your product design. A single piece of research might supply you with one thing that will affect your design or several things, depending upon what the research involved. One useful approach is to ensure that every item of research ends with an explanation of how it is affecting your design. For example, '*As a result of this research, my design should be …*'.

Another way to do this is to ask yourself 'SO WHAT?' and then to answer it! For example, '*I have found that creases are used in pop up card mechanisms – SO WHAT? This means that on my design if I use creases the mechanism will work more efficiently and the folds will look neat and crisp.*'

If you make a list of the requirements that you have identified at the end of each piece of research, these can be used as the basis for your specification. This is a list of all the key needs that your product must meet; there will probably be at least 10 different needs in this list, and often 15–20. It can be very helpful to word process this list, as you will use it several times during the design process.

Remember that the specification is a list of requirements that your product should have. It should not give the answer to your problem. For example, if you were designing a new storage container, at this stage you should not state that it is a bag as this would limit the opportunity to consider boxes, tins, cupboards etc.

16.3 Development of the design proposal

In this section of your folder you are expected to generate a range of design ideas and develop these into a final product.

The assessment criteria for the development of the design proposal are shown in Table 16.3.

Criterion 2 mark band	Development of design proposals (including modelling)
26–32	○ Imaginative and innovative ideas have been developed, demonstrating creativity, flair and originality. Further developments made to take account of ongoing research ○ A coherent and appropriate design strategy, with clear evidence of a planned approach, adopted throughout ○ The implications of a wide range of issues including social, moral, environmental and sustainability, are taken into consideration and inform the development of the design proposals ○ Excellent development work through experimentation with a wide variety of techniques and modeling (including CAD where appropriate) in order to produce a final design solution ○ Appropriate materials/ingredients and components selected with full regard to their working properties ○ Fully detailed and justified product/manufacturing specification taking full account of the analysis undertaken
19–25	○ Imaginative ideas demonstrating a degree of creativity, which are further developed to take account of ongoing research ○ An appropriate design strategy, with evidence of planning, adopted for most aspects ○ Development of design proposals take into account the main aspects relating to a variety of social, moral, environmental and sustainability issues ○ Good development work achieved through working with a variety of techniques and modeling (including CAD where appropriate) ○ Appropriate materials/ingredients and components selected with regard to their working properties ○ Product/manufacturing specification is complete and reflects key aspects of the analysis undertaken

△ **Table 16.2** Development of design proposals   *Contd*

Criterion 2 mark band	Development of design proposals (including modelling)
12–18	○ Design ideas show some degree of creativity and further development ○ An appropriate design strategy, with some evidence of planning, adopted for some aspects ○ Developments of design solutions are influenced to some extent by factors relating to social, moral, environmental and sustainability issues ○ Adequate development work achieved through working with a range of techniques and modelling (including CAD where appropriate) ○ Materials/ingredients and components selected with some regard to their working properties ○ Product/manufacturing specification reflects most aspects of the analysis
6–11	○ Ideas show some variation in approach or concept ○ A limited design strategy, with minimal planning, is evident ○ Some consideration taken of social, moral, environmental and sustainability issue in development of design solutions ○ Development work is lacking in detail but makes reference to a number of techniques and modelling (including CAD where appropriate) ○ Materials/ingredients and components selected with limited regard to their working properties ○ Limited product/manufacturing specification which reflects most obvious features of analysis
0–5	○ Ideas are lacking in imagination with minimal development or further research ○ Little evidence of a logical approach being adopted, with no indication of planning ○ Development work shows little consideration of social, moral, environmental and sustainability issues ○ Basic development work undertaken using a limited range of techniques ○ Materials/ingredients and components selected with little regard to their working properties ○ Produced a simple product/manufacturing specification which is general in nature

△ **Table 16.2** Development of design proposals

This section is the creation of your ideas through to the final design. This should involve several steps, which might include planning your project, sketching ideas, using models to further develop and test your thinking and ideas, and producing a detailed manufacturing specification and production plan.

It is a good idea to start this section by producing a planning chart, such as a Gantt chart. This lists the tasks to be carried out, how long each task will take and when it will be carried out. This helps you to identify the tasks that you will need to complete and manage the time you have. This is particularly important in a Controlled Assessment situation, as the time to complete the project is limited to approximately 45 hours in total – if one activity is allowed to take too long, it might mean that you will not have the time to complete your project, which could have a significant impact on the grade that you achieve.

If used correctly the planning chart can also help you prepare for each lesson, as you will be able to identify the tools, equipment and materials that you will need to use and check that they are available.

The first step in capturing your design ideas is normally sketching. A common error during the generation of ideas is to focus just on your first idea idea, or a very limited number of designs, and to decide to use that for your final product. Even if you have a strong preference for one idea, you should aim for at least five or six different ideas. For example, if designing an educational toy on a transport theme, six different types of car would probably be too similar. Whereas a car, a boat, an aeroplane, a lorry, a horse cart and a travel game would clearly show the examiner that you have a good variety of ideas.

When producing your design ideas, remember that you are trying to communicate them to the client. Use recognised drawing styles to illustrate your ideas; this could include isometric and perspective drawings. Key features should be labelled and explained to show your design thinking; these should include references to:

o   the materials that could be used
o   how the idea could be made
o   where ergonomics have influenced your design thinking
o   environmental issues related to the product, such as how it could be disposed of or recycled at the end of its life
o   any social or moral issues relating to the manufacture or use of the product.

You might even use close-up views of some details, sectional views and cut-away views to make sure that anyone who sees the idea has a clear understanding of what you mean. One way to check your communication is to show an idea to someone else in your class, and get them to explain to you what it means – they should not judge the idea, just explain what they understand it to be.

Exam tip

A small choice of materials drawn next to your ideas is a good way to show how you have compared materials. A reason for choice of selection next to this further illustrates your knowledge and understanding.

Once you have a range of ideas you need to choose at least one to be developed for your final design. One way of choosing is to compare each of your ideas against thee needs in your specification, and see which is the 'best fit'. During your analysis of these initial designs you might find that your ideas do not always meet the points of the specification; problems will be found. At this point make sketches of the solutions to these issues to support your reasoning in the design process.

Modelling is an important approach to develop your chosen idea into a final design proposal. These can be CAD models, 2D card models, 3D Styrofoam models or even models manufactured using rapid prototyping equipment. These models might be used for several different pieces of information – for example, to work out the sizes and ergonomic features of your design, to check that parts will fit together, or to check that manufacturing processes will be able to make it.

Knowledge link

For more information on rapid prototyping, please refer to Chapter 11.

When you make a model, you should take a picture to provide evidence for your portfolio. In order to achieve the higher level of assessment it should be evidenced that you have used these models to inform, change and develop your design. This can be achieved by adding labels to the models, explaining how well they worked and how your design will be changed to improve its performance. Possible design changes can also be sketched on to the photograph, to show changes that you intend to make to your design.

Once you have a design that fully meets the needs of your specification and you are happy with it, you should present it in a way that your design could be used by someone else to make it. This can be achieved by preparing the following documents, which will provide good evidence in your folder:

o Dimensioned drawings – a manufacturer needs to know the sizes to be able to make a part. The drawing should be drawn in third-angle orthographic projection; CAD software can be used to do this, if available.

o Parts list – you should identify the materials and components that are needed to make your product. This can be either a separate table or included on the working drawing, either as labels or as a table.

o Production plan – this is a stage-by-stage guide of every process that will be used in the manufacture of your product. The plan can be completed as a table. Headings must include materials, equipment used, safety requirements, quality checks and time allocation.

o A product manufacturing specification – this is a development of your earlier specification. It shows where each of the design criteria is affected during the manufacturing process. One way of avoiding duplication is to include references to the relevant steps in your production plan.

16.4 Making

In this part of your Controlled Assessment, you will make the product that you designed. The assessment criteria for making are given in Table 16.4.

Criterion 3 mark band	Making
26–32	o Final outcome(s) shows a high level of making/modelling/finishing skills and accuracy o Selected and used appropriate tools, materials and/or technologies including, where appropriate, CAM correctly, skillfully and safely o Worked independently to produce a rigorous and demanding outcome o Quality controls are evident throughout the project and it is clear how accuracy has been achieved. o The outcome has the potential to be commercially viable and is suitable for the target market
19–25	o Final outcome shows very good level of making/modelling/finishing skills o Selected and used appropriate tools, materials and/or technologies including, where appropriate, CAM correctly and safely o Outcome demonstrates a high level of demand o Quality control checks applied in the manufacture of the product o The outcome is suitable for the target market and could be commercially viable with further development

△ **Table 16.4** Making

Contd

Criterion 3 mark band	Making
12–18	○ Final outcome shows good level of making/modelling/finishing skills ○ Used appropriate materials, components, equipment and processes correctly and safely (including CAM) ○ Parts of outcome show high levels of demand ○ Applied quality control checks broadly but superficially ○ The outcome requires further development in order to be suitable for the target market
6–11	○ Final outcome is largely complete and represents a basic level of making/modelling/finishing skills ○ Used materials, components and equipment correctly and safely (including CAM if appropriate) ○ Some aspects of outcome are demanding ○ Some evidence of limited quality control applied throughout the process ○ The outcome has some weaknesses which limit its suitability for the target market
0–5	○ Final outcome is incomplete or represents an undemanding level of making/modelling/finishing skills ○ Used materials, components and equipment safely under close supervision ○ Worked with some assistance to produce outcome of limited demand ○ There is limited evidence of any quality control and levels of accuracy are minimal ○ The outcome has significant weaknesses which limit its suitability for the target market

△ **Table 16.4** Making

Many people assume that all the marks for this section are given just for the quality of the manufactured piece. This is incorrect. While the quality of the making and the finished product are awarded marks, within the body of your folder you should also illustrate how you have used and selected the right materials and manufacturing techniques, and how you have checked and tested quality issues. Evidence for these might come from:

○ your production plan, as outlined in the previous section
○ pictures of making the product, with comments explaining what you were doing and why

○ a picture of your finished product, with labels pointing out key features and details, and comments on their accuracy and quality
○ test records for any quality checks made.

To achieve high marks for this section you need to demonstrate the accurate use of a wide range of manufacturing skills. The more challenging and complex your product is, the easier it is to demonstrate your range of skills. If you have a very simple design it will be difficult to build in a high level of making skills and use of a variety of materials and manufacturing processes. At the design stage it is a good idea to reflect on this and ensure that your design meets the requirements of the brief and the demands of the making outcome.

16.5 **Testing and evaluation**

This part of your Controlled Assessment covers both evaluation throughout the design process and the testing of the final product. The assessment criteria for testing and evaluating are shown in Table 16.5.

Criterion 4 mark band	Testing and evaluation
9–12	<ul><li>Detailed testing and evaluation as appropriate throughout the designing and making process taking account of client/user or third party opinion</li><li>All aspects of the final outcome have been tested against the design criteria and/or the product/manufacturing specification</li><li>Evaluate and justify the need for modifications to the product and consideration given as to how the outcome might need to be modified for commercial production</li></ul>
6–8	<ul><li>Appropriate testing and evaluation evident throughout the designing and making process</li><li>Most aspects of the final outcome have been tested against the design criteria and/ or the product/manufacturing specification</li><li>Evaluate and justify the need for improvements or modifications to the product</li></ul>
3–5	<ul><li>Evidence of some testing and evaluation leading to the production of the final outcome</li><li>Some evidence of testing against the design criteria and/or the product/manufacturing specification</li><li>Some improvements or modifications to product suggested</li></ul>
0–3	<ul><li>Minimal testing and evaluation throughout the designing and making process</li><li>Limited or no testing of final outcome against the design criteria and/or the product/manufacturing specification</li><li>Limited mention of some improvements or modifications that could be made to the product</li></ul>

△ **Table 16.5** Testing and evaluation

Testing and evaluation is assessed throughout the whole of the Design and Make project. When developing your design add evaluative comments, compare ideas against the specification and find ways of testing your product. You are expected to show the outline of the tests and most importantly the results and as a consequence your decisions.

You should compare your final product against each point in your specification. Ideally this should be carried out using objective testing methods, based on data and facts rather than opinions. If your product varies from the requirements of the specification, you should explain any differences. This can help to provide evidence that you have evaluated the need for any modifications to the product. Additional evidence can also be provided by labelling a picture of your finished product, explaining where modifications or improvements could be made.

16.6 Communication

Communication refers to the overall contents of your folder. The assessment criteria are shown in Table 16.6.

Criterion 5 mark band	Communication
5–6	○ Design folder is focused, concise and relevant and demonstrates an appropriate selection of material for inclusion ○ All decisions communicated in a clear and coherent manner with appropriate use of technical language ○ The text is legible, easily understood and shows a good grasp of grammar, punctuation and spelling
3–4	○ Design folder shows some skill in choice of material for inclusion but includes some irrelevant content ○ Most decisions communicated with some clarity and with some use of technical language ○ There are a small number of errors in grammar, punctuation and spelling
0–2	○ Design folder shows excessive duplication of information and a lack of brevity and focus resulting in irrelevant content ○ Ideas and decisions communicated at a simplistic level with a limited grasp of the concepts involved and a limited use of technical vocabulary ○ Numerous errors in grammar, punctuation and spelling

△ **Table 16.6** Communication

Some people incorrectly assume that the communication marks are awarded mainly for the appearance of the folder. They may spend several hours adding borders and colour schemes. This is not an effective use of the limited time available.

The communication mark is given for the overall clarity, relevance, look, layout and general presentation of the folder. It should be focused, concise and relevant.

You should ensure there is a wide range of accurate, detailed and illustrative skills. It is important to use technical terms throughout your folder. Your writing should be legible, clear and in good English, with correct spelling, and making good use of punctuation and grammar. Many of these aspects can be aided by the use of a word processor.

16.7 Further examples of Controlled Assessment work

Examples of Controlled Assessment work are given throughout this book to show you how the knowledge and understanding you need for the written examination are also important and relevant to your Controlled Assessment. This section shows some further examples from students' folders to inspire you when working on your own Controlled Assessment.

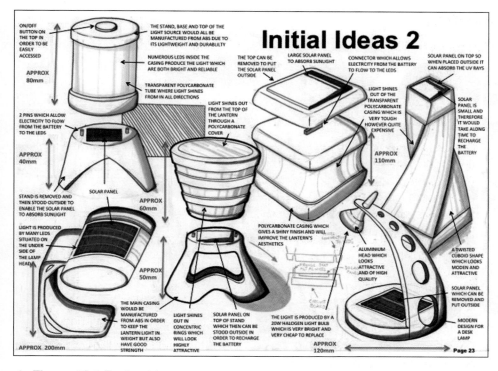

△ **Figure 16.1** Design ideas

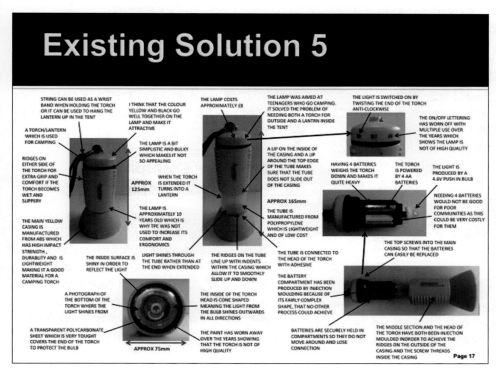

△ **Figure 16.2** Analysis of existing solutions

△ **Figure 16.3** Development

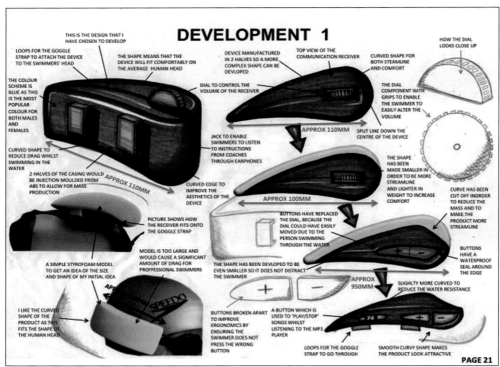

△ **Figure 16.4** Development

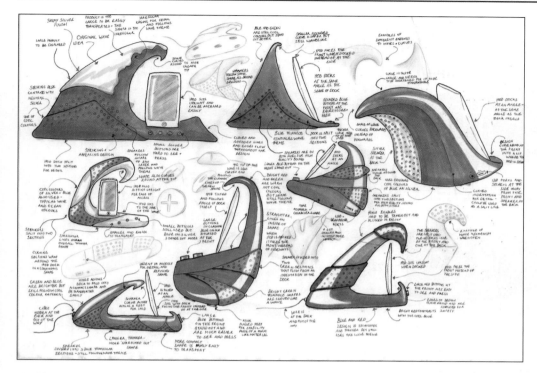

△ **Figure 16.5** Development

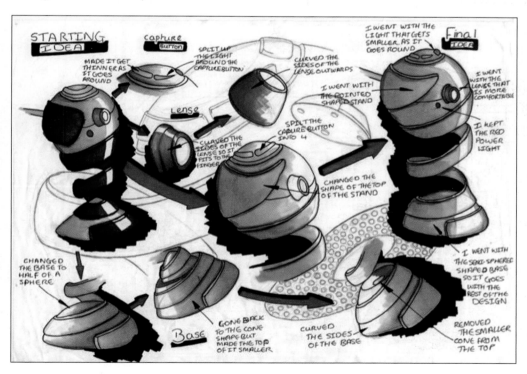

△ **Figure 16.6** Development

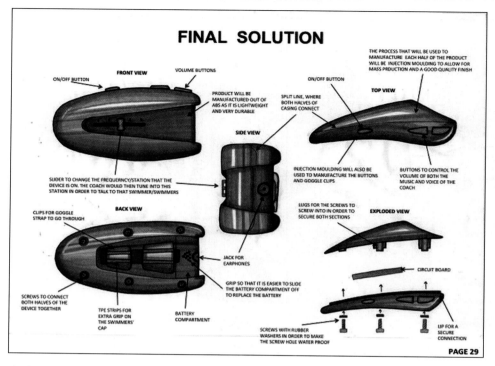

△ **Figure 16.7** Final solution

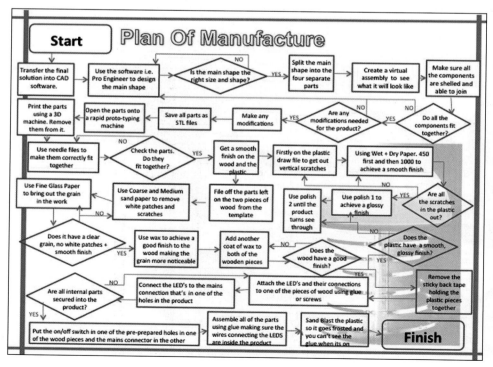

△ **Figure 16.8** Plan of manufacture

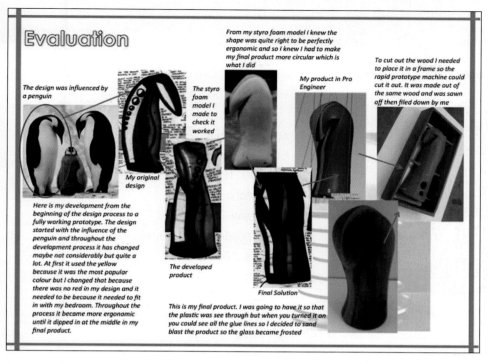

Evaluation

From my styro foam model I knew the shape was quite right to be perfectly ergonomic and so I knew I had to make my final product more circular which is what I did

My product in Pro Engineer

To cut out the wood I needed to place it in a frame so the rapid prototype machine could cut it out. It was made out of the same wood and was sawn off then filed down by me

The design was influenced by a penguin

The styro foam model I made to check it worked

My original design

Here is my development from the beginning of the design process to a fully working prototype. The design started with the influence of the penguin and throughout the development process it has changed maybe not considerably but quite a lot. At first it used the yellow because it was the most popular colour but I changed that because there was no red in my design and it needed to be because it needed to fit in with my bedroom. Throughout the process it became more ergonomic until it dipped in at the middle in my final product.

The developed product

Final Solution

This is my final product. I was going to have it so that the plastic was see through but when you turned it on you could see all the glue lines so I decided to sand blast the product so the glass became frosted

△ **Figure 16.9** Evaluation

Evaluation

Target Market and User Requirements
(from both Design Brief and Specification)

-The most important issue in my brief was that it was a **'lamp, preferably a mood lamp'** because that was what they wanted me to design, which I have done. Also in my specification I mentioned, it should be, **'if possible lighted internally'**, which it is because inside the blue acrylic there is LED's which make the product seem to glow. This is perfect especially seeing as in my specification it wasn't supposed to be purely practical, i.e. giving off as much light as possible, but a decorative purpose as well because my target market preferred it to be **'more decorative than practical.'** Also, another important issue in my brief was that it would be **'unique'** because then it would stand out more on the self from the other products and I think my product is definitely unique as it is the only penguin mood lamp.

This is the way it will work. By using LED's attached to the wood, the light will shine out through the see-through plastic

-My target market was supposed to be **'females between 14 and 25'**. I think that I have kept in accordance to this because people liked my product. Also, males have said they like the product also, so by using more neutral colours of red and a rich brown, I have unintentionally managed to widen my target market, as it was only meant for girls to start off with, it will bring in more profit because more people want to buy it. However, it was also important that it wasn't that expensive because as my target market consists mainly of students, they don't have a lot of money. The way it is designed the back pieces of plastic are both curved, making the wood curved also, which makes it both more expensive to manufacture and more time consuming. This doesn't keep to my brief and specification because I wanted it to be both **'preferably between £10-20'** and **'cheap and quick way of manufacture'** and it isn't at the moment, so if it was to be mass produced I would make the plastic pieces straight, making it cheaper.

The colours of red, blue and brown appeal to my target sex of female but also could widen my target market

Here is how it is internally lit. Also, you can see that it is unique as there is no other mood lamps like this

△ **Figure 16.10** Evaluation

Index

Page numbers in **bold** show key concepts.